Famous Functions
in Number Theory

IAS/PCMI—The Teacher Program Series
Mathematics for Teaching: A Problem-Based Approach

Famous Functions in Number Theory

Bowen Kerins • Darryl Yong • Al Cuoco • Glenn Stevens

American Mathematical Society
Institute for Advanced Study
Park City Mathematics Institute

Mathematics for Teaching: A Problem-Based Resource for Teachers was developed at Education Development Center, Inc. (EDC) in partnership with the Park City Mathematics Institute (PCMI), with the support of the National Science Foundation.

Development Team: Bowen Kerins, Darryl Yong, Al Cuoco, Glenn Stevens

2010 *Mathematics Subject Classification.* Primary 00-01; Secondary 00A07.

For additional information and updates on this book, visit
www.ams.org/bookpages/sstp-3

Library of Congress Cataloging-in-Publication Data

Mathematics for teaching : a problem-based approach / Bowen Kerins [and three others].
volumes cm.—(IAS/PCMI, the teacher program series)

"Institute for Advanced Study."
"Park City Mathematics Institute."
"Developed at Education Development Center, Inc. (EDC) in partnership with the Park City Mathematics Institute (PCMI), with support of the National Science Foundation."

Based on a summer series of workshops held in 2009.

Includes bibliographical references.

Contents: volume 1. Probability through algebra—volume 2. Applications of algebra and geometry to the work of teaching—volume 3. Famous functions in number theory

ISBN 978-1-4704-2195-3 (alk. paper)

1. Mathematics teachers—Training of—Congresses. 2. Mathematics—Study and teaching—Congresses 3. Algebra—Congresses. 4. Probabilities—Congresses. 5. Number theory—Congresses. I. Kerins, Bowen, 1975– II. Institute for Advanced Study (Princeton, N.J.) III. Park City Mathematics Institute.

QA11.A1M23445   2015
510.71–dc23   2015022685

Others who contributed include: Gail Burrill, Margaret Cagle, Matt Enlow, John Mahoney, Sarah Sword, and Kevin Waterman.

Cover art courtesy of Karl Rubin, using MegaPOV, which is based on POV-Ray, both of which are open source, freely available software.

Contents

Preface

"To Think Deeply about Simple Things" was a motto of Arnold Ross, founder of the Ross Mathematics Program. Ross's philosophy has provided inspiration for many content-based professional development programs, each with its own personality and design, including the Summer School Teacher Program (SSTP) at the Park City Mathematics Institute (PCMI) and the PROMYS for Teachers Program (PfT) at Boston University.

More information about the SSTP can be found at mathforum.org/pcmi/hstp. For PfT, see www.promys.org/pft/.

PCMI, sponsored by the Institute for Advanced Study, is a three-week summer program for those involved in mathematics: research mathematicians, graduate students, undergraduate faculty, undergraduate students, and precollege teachers.

The SSTP has been an integral part of PCMI from the beginning. Since 2001, the mathematics course has been designed for precollege teachers by a collaborative of teachers, educators, and mathematicians from PfT. The SSTP course meets for 15 two-hour sessions during which the teachers investigate an aspect of mathematics loosely related to the overall mathematical theme of that summer's PCMI.

This book is based on the program from 2009, *Famous Functions in Number Theory*. One goal of this course is to introduce participants to the use of formal algebra in number theory. Through numerical experiments, participants learn how to use polynomial algebra as a bookkeeping mechanism that allows them to count divisors, build multiplicative functions, and compile multiplicative functions in a certain way that produces new ones. One capstone of the investigations is a beautiful result attributed to Fermat that determines the number of ways

Another goal, one that runs across all the summers, is to take up mathematics that helps teachers put the topics in their curricula into the broader landscape of mathematics as a scientific discipline.

a positive integer can be written as a sum of perfect squares.

The Design of the Course

The central feature of the SSTP course is a set of intricately sequenced questions that engage participants in doing mathematics in ways that exemplify the *Common Core* Standards for Mathematical Practice. What's important here is the structure of the program, because the program is not a "course" in the traditional sense. The materials provide participants with the opportunity for authentic mathematical discovery—participants build mathematical structures by investigating patterns, use reasoning to test and formalize their ideas, offer and negotiate mathematical definitions, and apply their theories and mathematical machinery to solve problems. Through this experience, participants develop habits of mind for thinking about and doing mathematics, deepening their mathematical intuition, sense-making, and reasoning skills.

The problem sets are separated into three sections: Important Stuff, Neat Stuff, and Tough Stuff. The problems in Important Stuff contain the fundamental concepts that should enable everyone to move forward. The problems in Neat Stuff and Tough Stuff are there for those who are curious or looking for a challenge.

The distinguishing features of the program have stayed constant over the years:

Teachers as professionals These materials are designed and implemented by practicing teachers in collaboration with mathematicians and mathematics educators. Experienced teachers mentor teachers new to the program by acting as "table leaders." The connections between the program and the teaching profession are real, because teachers are involved at every level.

Serious mathematics connected to secondary teaching Each experience is designed to connect to the mathematics teachers use in their professional lives. This "applied" mathematics is sometimes around underpinnings that will end up in the hands of students. But it may also take up mathematics that helps teachers put the topics in their curricula into the broader mathematical landscape.

Experience before formality Participants experience first-hand the effectiveness of struggling with new

---

Each fall and spring, a team drawn from the PfT community meets regularly to create two or three major themes for the upcoming SSTP course, and for each theme, it creates a "soup" of potential problems and investigations that might be used at PCMI. Once in Park City, the instructors create daily problem sets, revised each night to reflect what happened in the day's session. After the course, the problem sets are revised once more, solutions and hints are written, and the course is prepared for publication.

In one summer at the SSTP, teachers studied how formal algebra with polynomials can be used to bring coherence to combinatorial problems. In another summer, teachers learned to apply the arithmetic of algebraic numbers to the problem of designing tasks for their students that "come out nice."

ideas and connections *before* they are brought to closure. The role of the instructor is to pull together the participants at several points to collate conjectures, logical arguments, and extensions. With help from those around them, teachers refine and prove their own conjectures, sometimes over the course of several days. This style of learning, emblematic of the intent of the *Common Core's* Standards for Mathematical Practice, has had an immense effect on how teachers approach their own classes and how they view the discipline they teach.

The goal of the PCMI teacher program is to provide teachers with opportunities to:

- deepen their understanding of mathematics,

- reflect on the practice of teaching, and

- serve as mathematical resources for their colleagues.

All of this has worked. Exit reviews of the summer programs and in-depth interviews by external evaluators of teachers from varying backgrounds and school systems have provided evidence that the program has helped hundreds of teachers become more effective in—and more satisfied with—their professional lives. According to one evaluation report, many participants have been influenced by PCMI to revise their roles as teachers, acting more as facilitators, rebalancing how much time they allow students to talk versus talking themselves, and giving students more responsibility for their own learning. They consciously change the ways they question students and answer questions, and make reasoning and sense making a core goal of their instruction.

While these materials were developed for use at the SSTP, they have been piloted in other settings and have been successfully adapted for use as a capstone course for preservice mathematics teachers and as an elective in a mathematics or mathematics education program where students did one problem set per week. While the course does not replace a standard number theory course, it prepares students to take such a course, with the problem sets building towards a mathematical conclusion. The materials could be used as a course in a graduate program or summer institute for teachers, or in a variety of different professional development configurations. Intermediate conclusions typically occur every four or five problem sets, so a shortened course might consist of the first four

Teachers work in tables of 5–6 participants, accompanied by a table leader who typically responds to questions with well-posed additional questions. Tablemates work on carefully crafted problem sets, slowly abstracting general principles from calculations and experiments.

Teachers meet after each mathematical session to discuss the work of teaching. One summer focused on how to make classrooms a place where questioning is central to learning. In another summer, participants considered how to manage discourse that made students the center of the discussion. Activities are designed around artifacts of practice, such as student work, classroom videos, assessment, or lesson design.

or five problem sets or the eighth or ninth problem sets. In settings where credit is offered, some instructors have assigned projects or reports on specified readings related to the work. While the mathematics may seem appropriate only for teachers with a strong mathematical background, it was designed to provide all teachers with a rich mathematical experience, regardless of their backgrounds.

Navigating the Problem Sets

To allow access for multiple levels of experience, any topic in algebra or beyond is approached as though it is newly encountered. For example, the work on quadratics is designed to lead to an understanding of the quadratic formula, not requiring it, and generalizations come from repeated iterations of examples, not from an initial exposure. Many learners find their first answers by testing options, and when an unusual one comes along, they use the patterns from their previous work to figure out what might happen in this new case. In some cases, the proof uses all of the key ideas from the openers (boxed problems). The problems are not built to support a lecture but rather deliberately constructed for students to pursue a general solution over time, with the goal of enabling the learners to build their own understanding from the problems as they work through them.

Note that because the problems are carefully crafted to let the mathematics unfold through the experience of actually doing the work, facilitators should do all of the problems, at least in Important Stuff, themselves before engaging students so as to anticipate students' thought processes and to encourage them during explorations and discoveries.

A few things are important about how the materials are structured:

- The boxed openers are meant to be answered just like the rest of the problems. Consider them "Problem 0"; they are boxed because they are intended to be more important than others. A general note: keep looking forward in the problem sets. The solutions do not go immediately for proof, but rather the course tends to let ideas sit for a while. For example, a proof of the Problem Set 3 opener might be found in a problem in Problem Set 4.

- There are problem categories: *Important Stuff*, *Neat Stuff*, *Tough Stuff*, and maybe other stuff sometimes.

All the mathematics that is central to the program can be found and developed in the Important Stuff. That's why it's Important Stuff.

- As mentioned earlier, the materials provide experience before formality, where the participant uses examples to build intuition. Definitions and theorems appear as capstones, not foundations.

- The problems should lead to the appropriate mathematics rather than requiring it. The same goes for technology: the problems should lead to the appropriate use of technology rather than requiring it.

- The problems have multiple points of entry where everyone, regardless of their level of confidence or experience, can begin.

- The materials have a low threshold and a high ceiling—they allow everyone to experience success and are also designed so that participants will feel challenged regardless of skill or experience level.

- The problems explicitly link different content areas and encourage participants to seek multiple representations and solutions.

- A problem presented from one perspective (algebraically, say) may be repeated in another (geometrically, for example).

- The problems often foreshadow key ideas that are not introduced formally until later problem sets.

- The problems repeat and connect throughout all of the sets. A goal is to have the participants look for connections rather than being surprised when they notice relationships.

CHAPTER

1

Problem Sets

Welcome to the class.

We know you'll learn a great deal of mathematics here—maybe some new tricks, maybe some new perspectives on things with which you're already familiar. A few things you should know about how the class is organized:

- **Don't worry about answering all the questions.** If you're answering every question, we haven't written the problem sets correctly.

  Some of the problems have yet to be solved. It's especially good to think about these.

- **Don't worry about getting to a certain problem number.** Some participants have been known to spend all their energy on a particular set working on one problem (and perhaps a few of its extensions or consequences).

- **Stop and smell the roses.** Getting the correct answer to a question is not a be-all and end-all in this course. How does the question relate to others you've encountered? How do others think about this question?

- **Respect everyone's views.** Remember that you have something to learn from everyone else. Remember that everyone works at a different pace.

- **Teach only if you have to.** You may feel the temptation to teach others in your group. Fight it! We don't mean you should ignore your classmantes but give everyone the chance to discover. If you think it's a good time to teach your colleagues about the Law of Cosines, think again: the problems should lead to the appropriate mathematics rather than requiring it. The same goes for technology: the problems should lead to the appropriate use of technology rather than requiring it.

- **Each problem set has its Stuff.** There are problem categories: Important Stuff, Neat Stuff, Tough Stuff, and maybe other stuff sometimes. Check out Important Stuff first. All the mathematics that is central to the course can be found and developed in the Important Stuff. *That's* why it's Important Stuff. Everything else is just neat or tough. If you didn't get through the Important Stuff, we probably noticed... and that question will be seen again soon. Each problem set is based on what happened in the previous set, and what happened in the previous *class*.

When you start working through Problem Set 3, come back and read this introduction again.

Will you remember? Maybe. . .

Problem Set 1

Opener

Every positive integer has divisors, numbers that divide evenly into it. The divisors of 4 are 1, 2, and 4. The divisors of 18 are 1, 2, 3, 6, 9, and 18. In this Problem Set, you will investigate a function called σ, which takes in a positive integer, and returns the *sum* of all its divisors. For example, $\sigma(4) = 7$ and $\sigma(18) = 39$.

The Opener problems are important!

Here's a large table for the σ function. Complete the table without help from a calculator or computer.

n	1	2	3	4	5	6	7	8	9	10	11	12
$\sigma(n)$				7								

n	13	14	15	16	17	18	19	20	21	22	23	24
$\sigma(n)$												

n	25	26	27	28	29	30	31	32	33	34	35	36
$\sigma(n)$												

n	37	38	39	40	41	42	43	44	45	46	47	48
$\sigma(n)$												

n	49	50	51	52	53	54	55	56	57	58	59	60
$\sigma(n)$					54							

n	61	62	63	64	65	66	67	68	69	70	71	72
$\sigma(n)$												

n	73	74	75	76	77	78	79	80	81	82	83	84
$\sigma(n)$												

n	85	86	87	88	89	90	91	92	93	94	95	96
$\sigma(n)$												

Important Stuff

Each Problem Set is divided into Important Stuff, Neat Stuff, and Tough Stuff—and the Opener, which is more important than any of the rest.

1. Describe some patterns in the table for the σ function, especially patterns that helped you complete the table quickly, or patterns you could use to find other outputs.

2. Determine each of the following without technology.

   Why might part (c) be written as $5 \cdot 49$ instead of 245?

   a. $\sigma(128)$ **b.** $\sigma(243)$ **c.** $\sigma(5 \cdot 49)$ **d.** $\sigma(257)$ **e.** $\sigma(1001)$

3. Define $A(n) = \frac{\sigma(n)}{n}$. Use a calculator if you find it helpful here.

   a. Find all numbers n with $A(n) \leqslant 1$.
   b. Find three numbers n with $A(n) = 2$.
   c. Are there any numbers n with $A(n) = 3$?

Neat Stuff

Here are some more good questions to think about.

4. If p is prime, what can you say about $\sigma(p)$? About $A(p)$?

5. If p and q are primes, what can you say about $\sigma(pq)$? About $A(pq)$?

6. If p and q are primes, find the maximum possible value of $A(pq)$.

7. Without technology, find a number for which $\sigma(n) = 1000$ or show that no such number exists.

8. Find the maximum possible value of $A(n)$.

9. Go back to the problems on the previous page, except now use $\sigma_2(n)$, the sum of the *squares* of the divisors, and $B(n) = \frac{\sigma_2(n)}{n^2}$.

Tough Stuff

Here are two much more difficult problems to try.

10. Without using technology, find a number n for which $A(n) \geqslant 5$ or a proof that no such number exists.

11. Find an odd number for which $A(n) = 2$, or prove that no such number exists.

Problem Set 2

Opener

Problem Set 1 focused on the σ function, which outputs the sum of the divisors of its input. In this Problem Set, you will explore a function called a, which takes in a positive integer, and returns the sum of its divisors' *reciprocals*. For example, $a(12) = \frac{1}{1} + \frac{1}{2} + \frac{1}{3} + \frac{1}{4} + \frac{1}{6} + \frac{1}{12} = \frac{7}{3}$.

Here's a table for the a function. Complete the table without using a calculator. Write answers in "lowest terms."

n	1	2	3	4	5	6	7	8	9	10	11	12
$a(n)$												$\frac{7}{3}$

n	13	14	15	16	17	18	19	20	21	22	23	24
$a(n)$												

n	25	26	27	28	29	30	31	32	33	34	35	36
$a(n)$												

n	37	38	39	40	41	42	43	44	45	46	47	48
$a(n)$												

Important Stuff

1. Determine each of the following.
   a. $a(3) \cdot a(4)$
   b. $a(2) \cdot a(5)$
   c. $a(8) \cdot a(15)$
   d. $a(120)$
   e. $a(10) \cdot a(12)$

2. Determine each of the following without using a calculator.
   a. $\left(1 + \frac{1}{3}\right)\left(1 + \frac{1}{2} + \frac{1}{4}\right)$
   b. $\left(1 + \frac{1}{2}\right)\left(1 + \frac{1}{5}\right)$

c. $\left(1 + \frac{1}{2} + \frac{1}{4} + \frac{1}{8}\right)\left(1 + \frac{1}{3} + \frac{1}{5} + \frac{1}{15}\right)$

d. $\left(1 + \frac{1}{2} + \frac{1}{5} + \frac{1}{10}\right)\left(1 + \frac{1}{2} + \frac{1}{3} + \frac{1}{4} + \frac{1}{6} + \frac{1}{12}\right)$

3. Calculate each of the following any way you like.

   a. $1 + \frac{1}{2}$

   b. $1 + \frac{1}{2} + \frac{1}{4}$

   c. $\frac{1}{2^0} + \frac{1}{2^1} + \frac{1}{2^2} + \frac{1}{2^3}$

   d. $\frac{1}{2^0} + \frac{1}{2^1} + \frac{1}{2^2} + \cdots \frac{1}{2^6}$

   e. The sum of all numbers in the form $\frac{1}{2^n}$ as n goes from 0 to 10

   f. $\displaystyle\sum_{n=0}^{11} \frac{1}{2^n}$

   The notation in part (f) 3f says to sum $\frac{1}{2^n}$ for all n from 0 to 11. A good shorthand to learn.

   g. $\displaystyle\sum_{n=0}^{\infty} \frac{1}{2^n}$

4. Find the *smallest* possible number k for which you are completely sure that $k > a(n)$ for *all* powers of 3. In other words, k is the smallest number larger than all the numbers in the sequence

$$a(1), a(3), a(9), a(27), \ldots$$

Neat Stuff

5. For certain values of n, it turns out that $\sigma(n) = 3 + \frac{n}{2} + n$. Classify these numbers and find a generalization.

   Remember, the σ function is the sum of the divisors.

6. If p and q are primes, write a rule for $\sigma(pq)$ in terms of p and q.

7. If p and q are primes, write a rule for $a(pq)$ in terms of p and q and give the simplest answer you can.

8. Let n be any of the large set of numbers whose only prime factors are 2 and 3. ($n = 12$ and $n = 324$ are two examples.)

   a. Find the smallest possible number k for which you are completely sure that $k > a(n)$, no matter what n was picked.

   b. Find a suitable number n such that $k - a(n) < 0.1$.

9. Find the first ten numerators in the following bizarre-looking expansion. Do *not* try to simplify or combine terms, just expand!

$$\left(\frac{1}{1^x} + \frac{2}{2^x} + \frac{3}{3^x} + \frac{4}{4^x} + \cdots\right)\left(\frac{1}{1^x} + \frac{1}{2^x} + \frac{1}{3^x} + \frac{1}{4^x} + \cdots\right)$$

$$= \frac{?}{1^x} + \frac{?}{2^x} + \frac{?}{3^x} + \frac{?}{4^x} + \cdots$$

10. Find the first ten numerators in the following bizarre-looking expansion. Do *not* try to simplify or combine terms, just expand!

$$\left(\frac{1}{1^x} + \frac{4}{2^x} + \frac{9}{3^x} + \frac{16}{4^x} + \cdots\right)\left(\frac{1}{1^x} + \frac{1}{2^x} + \frac{1}{3^x} + \frac{1}{4^x} + \cdots\right)$$

$$= \frac{?}{1^x} + \frac{?}{2^x} + \frac{?}{3^x} + \frac{?}{4^x} + \cdots$$

Tough Stuff

11. Without using technology, find a number n for which $a(n) \geqslant 10$, or prove that no such number exists.

12. Find an odd number for which $a(n) = 2$, or prove that no such number exists.

Problem Set 3

Opener

The figure below tabulates the product xy for different values of x and y. How many of these numbers are multiples of 6? The function k(n) takes in an integer and returns the number of products xy that are multiples of n when x and y range from 0 to n − 1.

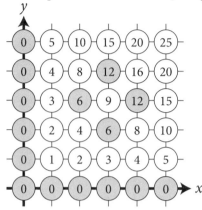

Based on the picture above, k(6) = 15.

Here's a table for the k function. Complete the table without a calculator or computer program. Use the handout at the end of this Problem Set (multiple copies may be needed), and others' help.

n	1	2	3	4	5	6	7	8	9	10	11	12
k(n)	1					15						

n	13	14	15	16	17	18	19	20	21	22	23	24
k(n)												

Important Stuff

1. Notice anything interesting about k(n)?

   Does this function share any properties seen in the functions used in Problem Sets 1 and 2?

2. a. Armando says that if a number is a multiple of 8 and a multiple of 15, then it must be a multiple of 120. What do you think?

b. Jennifer says that if a number is a multiple of 10 and a multiple of 12, then it must be a multiple of 120. What do you think?

3. Three of these four multiplication facts are correct. Use the units digit of each number to determine which of the four facts is *incorrect*.

    a. $234 \times 153 = 35802$
    b. $157 \times 321 = 50397$
    c. $223 \times 155 = 34565$
    d. $168 \times 183 = 30746$

4. When working with units digits you are working in "mod 10", a number system that considers only remainders when dividing by 10. In mod 10, the only numbers are 0 through 9. There are lots of other "mods" too.

    a. What is 4×3 in mod 10?
    b. What is 8×3 in mod 10?
    c. What is 8×3 in mod 12?
    d. What number solves $2x = 7$ in mod 9?
    e. What *two* numbers solve $x^2 = 7$ in mod 9?

> The answer isn't $\sqrt{7}$ here, since the only numbers in mod 9 are 0 through 8. But the answers you find do "act like" $\sqrt{7}$ in some way.

5. Consider this summation:

$$1 + \frac{1}{2} + \frac{1}{4} + \frac{1}{4} + \frac{1}{8} + \frac{1}{8} + \frac{1}{8} + \underbrace{\frac{1}{16} + \cdots + \frac{1}{16}}_{\text{8 of these}} + \cdots$$

where each term is repeated 1, then 2, then 4, then 8 times, and it goes on forever. What happens to the sum as you take more terms? Is there a limit to the maximum value of the sum?

6. A function f is called *multiplicative* if

$$f(ab) = f(a) \cdot f(b)$$

whenever a and b don't share any common factors higher than 1.

> Two numbers are called *relatively prime* when they do not share common factors greater than 1.

    a. Give three examples of multiplicative functions you've seen in this course.
    b. Give three more examples of multiplicative functions.

Neat Stuff

7. Demonstrate each of the following, any way you like.

    a. $1 + \dfrac{1}{2} + \dfrac{1}{4} + \dfrac{1}{8} + \cdots = 2$

b. $1 + \dfrac{1}{3} + \dfrac{1}{9} + \dfrac{1}{27} + \cdots = \dfrac{3}{2}$

c. $\dfrac{1}{4^0} + \dfrac{1}{4^1} + \dfrac{1}{4^2} + \dfrac{1}{4^3} + \cdots = \dfrac{4}{3}$

d. $\displaystyle\sum_{n=0}^{\infty} \dfrac{1}{5^n} = \dfrac{5}{4}$

e. $\displaystyle\sum_{n=0}^{\infty} \dfrac{1}{p^n} = \dfrac{p}{p-1}$

> This last bit isn't actually true all the time! You might investigate to figure out what numbers it *is* true for. In this course we will use this formula only with numbers that make it true.

8. Recall function $a(n)$ from Problem Set 2.

    a. What is the value of $a(72)$?

    b. What is the value of $a(8) \cdot a(9)$?

    c. Calculate

$$\left(1 + \frac{1}{2} + \frac{1}{4} + \frac{1}{8}\right)\left(1 + \frac{1}{3} + \frac{1}{9}\right)$$

    d. *Without performing the final addition,* expand the expression above. What do you notice?

> One of the terms in the expansion is $\frac{1}{18}$.

9. The function $\tau(n)$ is defined as the number of factors of n.

    a. Tabulate the τ function for $n = 1$ through 20.

    b. Is τ multiplicative? Can you prove it?

    c. Describe a way to calculate $\tau(n)$ for any integer n.

10. Let $n = 2^p 3^q$. Find some values of p and q that produce particularly large values of $a(n)$, then determine the maximum possible value of $a(n)$ for any number in this form.

11. Let $n = 2^p 3^q 4^r$. Determine the maximum possible value of $a(n)$ for any number in this form.

12. Let $n = 2^p 3^q 5^r$. Determine the maximum possible value of $a(n)$ for any number in this form.

13. Consider this summation:

$$1 + \frac{1}{2} + \frac{1}{3} + \frac{1}{4} + \frac{1}{5} + \frac{1}{6} + \frac{1}{7} + \frac{1}{8} + \frac{1}{9} + \frac{1}{10} + \cdots$$

What happens to the sum as you take more terms? Is there a limit to the maximum value of the sum?

> You may find something helpful earlier in this problem set.

14. Prove that for any n, $a(n!)$ is at least as large as the sum of the first n terms in the series of Problem 13.

15. Prove that there is no maximum value of $a(n)$.

16. Find the first ten numerators in each of these expansions. Notice anything?

For example, when you end
up seeing a term like $\frac{1}{2^x 3^x}$,
that's really $\frac{1}{6^x}$. But don't try
to simplify something like
$\frac{2}{2^x}$ to $\frac{1}{2^x-1}$, just leave it so
the denominators are all k^x.

a.

$$\left(\frac{1}{1^x} + \frac{1}{2^x} + \frac{1}{3^x} + \frac{1}{4^x} + \cdots\right)\left(\frac{1}{1^x} + \frac{1}{2^x} + \frac{1}{3^x} + \frac{1}{4^x} + \cdots\right)$$

$$= \frac{?}{1^x} + \frac{?}{2^x} + \frac{?}{3^x} + \frac{?}{4^x} + \cdots$$

b.

$$\left(\frac{1}{1^x} + \frac{2}{2^x} + \frac{3}{3^x} + \frac{4}{4^x} + \cdots\right)\left(\frac{1}{1^x} + \frac{1}{2^x} + \frac{1}{3^x} + \frac{1}{4^x} + \cdots\right)$$

$$= \frac{?}{1^x} + \frac{?}{2^x} + \frac{?}{3^x} + \frac{?}{4^x} + \cdots$$

c.

$$\left(\frac{1}{1^x} + \frac{1/2}{2^x} + \frac{1/3}{3^x} + \frac{1/4}{4^x} + \cdots\right)\left(\frac{1}{1^x} + \frac{1}{2^x} + \frac{1}{3^x} + \frac{1}{4^x} + \cdots\right)$$

$$= \frac{?}{1^x} + \frac{?}{2^x} + \frac{?}{3^x} + \frac{?}{4^x} + \cdots$$

17. Let $f(n)$ be the number of solutions to $x^2 = 7$ in
mod n. Figure out anything you can about this
function.

If $n < 7$ you will need to
adjust the equation to suit
the mod. For example, in
mod 5, the equation
becomes $x^2 = 2$.

18. Define $\sigma_2(n)$ to be the sum of the squares of the
divisors of n and $b(n)$ as the sum of the reciprocals
of the squares of the divisors of n.

    a. Tabulate the σ_2 function from 1 to 10.

    b. Find some interesting things about the σ_2
function.

    c. Find $\sigma_2(120)$ without a calculator.

Tough Stuff

19. For what primes p is 7 a perfect square in mod p?

20. Find the maximum possible value of $b(n)$, where
b is the function from Problem 18.

Handout — Problem Set 3

At each coordinate (x, y), write the value of xy.

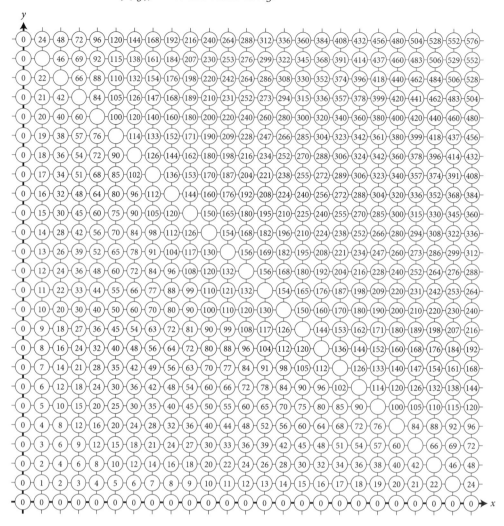

Problem Set 4

Opener

The figure below tabulates the product xy for values of x and y from 0 to 9. How many of these products are 1 more than a multiple of 10? Consider $P(n)$, which takes in an integer and returns the number of products xy that are *one more* than a multiple of n. Like in Problem Set 3, x and y range from 0 to $n - 1$.

You can use the table from Problem Set 3 here, too.

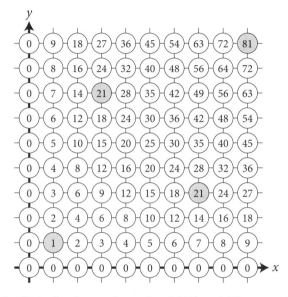

The shaded cells in the figure show that $P(10) = 4$. There are four products that are 1 more than a multiple of 10.

Complete this table for $P(n)$ using the handout along with any observations you make about the function's behavior.

Remember, for $P(9)$ you'd want to find numbers that are 1 more than a multiple of 9, and you'd only look for x and y ranging from 0 to 8.

n	1	2	3	4	5	6	7	8	9	10	11	12
P(n)	1		2					4		4		

n	13	14	15	16	17	18	19	20	21	22	23	24
P(n)												

Important Stuff

1. Notice anything interesting about $P(n)$?

2. Find a method that can be used to directly calculate $P(n)$ given the value of n, then use your method to find $P(210)$.

3. A function f is called *multiplicative* if

$$f(ab) = f(a) \cdot f(b)$$

whenever a and b don't share any common factors higher than 1.

If a and b share common factors, all bets are off!

 a. Give four examples of multiplicative functions you've seen in this course.
 b. Give one more example of a multiplicative function.
 c. Give three examples of functions that are *not* multiplicative.

4. a. Katie says that if a number is one more than a multiple of 8 and one more than a multiple of 15, then it must be one more than a multiple of 120. What do you think?
 b. Cliff says that if a number is one more than a multiple of 10 and one more than a multiple of 12, then it must be one more than a multiple of 120. What do you think?

5. In previous problem sets, we've defined many functions as the sum of something else across its divisors. Generally, define the *child s* of a function r by the following:

$$s(n) = r(\text{all divisors of } n) \text{ added together}$$
$$s(15) = r(1) + r(3) + r(5) + r(15)$$
$$s(20) = r(1) + r(2) + r(4) + r(5) + r(10) + r(20)$$
$$s(1) = r(1)$$

This definition can be applied to any function to produce a new "child function".

Let $r(n) = n$, and let s be the child of r.

 a. Calculate $s(15)$ and $s(20)$, then $s(1)$ through $s(10)$.
 b. Is r multiplicative? Does s seem to be multiplicative?
 c. By what name do you know s in this course?

6. Find all solutions to these equations. Reminder: in mod 7, the only possible answers are 0, 1, 2, 3, 4, 5, and 6.

As with other equations in algebra, there can be more than one solution, or even no solution.

 a. $3x = 4$ in mod 7   **b.** $6x = 4$ in mod 7
 c. $6x = 4$ in mod 8   **d.** $6x = 1$ in mod 8
 e. $x^2 = 2$ in mod 7   **f.** $x^3 = 1$ in mod 7
 g. $x^3 = -1$ in mod 7   **h.** $x^6 = 1$ in mod 7

Wait, -1 doesn't exist in mod 7... it's 6.

Neat Stuff

7. Many pairs of numbers have no common factor higher than 1: for example, 8 and 15. Function $\phi(n)$ returns the number of values from 1 to n that, when checked against n, have no common factor higher than 1.

   The greek letter ϕ is usually pronounced like "fee", but some say "fie".

   a. Show that $\phi(3) = 2$, $\phi(5) = 4$, and $\phi(15) = 8$.
   b. Calculate values of the ϕ function until you figure out what is happening.

8. Let $S = 1 + 5 + 5^2 + 5^3 + \cdots + 5^n$.

   a. Write an expression for $5S$.
   b. Write a clever expression for $4S$ by subtracting.
   c. Show that
   $$S = \frac{5^{n+1} - 1}{4}$$
   d. Find a general rule for $1 + x + x^2 + x^3 + \cdots + x^n$ in terms of x and n.

9. What is the child of $m(n) = 1$? (This function returns 1 for any input.)

   If you call the child $t(n)$, then $t(15) = m(1) + m(3) + m(5) + m(15)$.

10. Recall the k function from Problem Set 3. Find the child of k and tabulate its values. What patterns do you observe?

11. a. Find an equation that has *every number* as a solution in mod 7.
    b. Multiply this out and simplify it in mod 7:
    $$x(x-1)(x-2)(x-3)(x-4)(x-5)(x-6)$$

    On the TI-Nspire CAS, get a new calculator window using the HOME icon in the upper right, then select "expand" from the menus. Type out the expression you'd like to expand. "Simplify in mod 7" means that if you see 9x, write 2x.

12. Let $k_5(n)$ be the number of solutions to $xy = 5$ in mod n. Figure out anything you can about this function.

Tough Stuff

13. Prove that the P and ϕ functions must be identical. Specifically, prove that if a is relatively prime to n, then there is exactly one solution to $ab = 1 \bmod n$, and if a isn't relatively prime, there are no solutions.

14. For what primes p is 5 a perfect square in mod p?

15. What is the *grandparent* of $m(n) = 1$?

    You'll have to figure out how to determine the parent when given a child function. Twice...

16. Two circles with diameters a and b are tangent to a line and each other. A circle of diameter c is placed

as shown. Determine a nice relationship between a, b, and c.

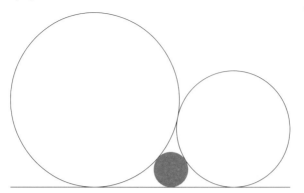

Problem Set 5

Opener

The ϕ function gives the number of values from 1 to n that are relatively prime to n; that is, those number that share no common factors greater than 1 with n. For example, $\phi(6) = 2$ since 1 and 5 don't share common factors with 6 (besides 1), while 2, 3, 4 do.

1. Determine $\phi(3)$, $\phi(5)$, and $\phi(15)$.

2. Determine $\phi(2)$, $\phi(7)$, and $\phi(14)$.

3. If p is a prime number, what is a formula for $\phi(p)$?

4. Determine a formula for $\phi(pq)$ where p and q are distinct primes.

Here's a table for $\phi(n)$ for $1 \leqslant n \leqslant 24$.

n	1	2	3	4	5	6	7	8	9	10	11	12
$\phi(n)$	1			2		2		4	6	4	10	4
n	13	14	15	16	17	18	19	20	21	22	23	24
$\phi(n)$	12			8	16	6	18	8	12	10	22	8

Let r be the child of ϕ, which was defined in Problem 1. Remember, if r is the child of ϕ it means that $r(3) = \phi(1) + \phi(3)$ and $r(10) = \phi(1) + \phi(2) + \phi(5) + \phi(10)$, among other things.

Complete this table for $r(n)$ from 1 to 24, and determine a rule for $r(n)$.

n	1	2	3	4	5	6	7	8	9	10	11	12
$r(n)$												
n	13	14	15	16	17	18	19	20	21	22	23	24
$r(n)$												

Amazing!

Important Stuff

1. Let $f(x) = \dfrac{1}{x}$. The *child* g of f is found by calculating

   $g(n) = f(\text{all divisors of } n) \text{ added together}$

   $g(15) = f(1) + f(3) + f(5) + f(15)$

   $g(20) = f(1) + f(2) + f(4) + f(5) + f(10) + f(20)$

   $g(1) = f(1)$

      a. Determine $g(3)$, $g(5)$, and $g(15)$.

      b. Determine $g(2)$, $g(7)$, and $g(14)$.

      c. If p is a prime number, what is a formula for $g(p)$?

2. Determine the grandchild of the ϕ function by finding the child of r.

3. Find all solutions for each of the following.

   a. $x^2 = x$ in mod 3   **b.** $x^2 = x$ in mod 5

   c. $x^2 = x$ in mod 7   **d.** $x^2 = x$ in mod 15

   e. $x^2 = x$ in mod 21   **f.** $x^2 = x$ in mod 35

   g. $x^2 = x$ in mod 105

   Be especially careful starting with part (d)!

Neat Stuff

4. Determine the child of $m(n) = 1$, a constant function.

5. Which of the following functions are multiplicative?

   a. $f(n) = n^2$ **b.** $g(n) = 2n$

   c. $m(n) = n$ mod 12   **d.** $a(n) = \frac{\sigma(n)}{n}$

   e. $y(n) = \gcd(n, 12)$

6. If f is a multiplicative function, what are the possible values of $f(1)$?

7. Is the sum of two multiplicative functions also multiplicative? What about the product?

8. Is the child of a multiplicative function also multiplicative?

   While no proof is expected here, you might think about how you would prove some of these. How are multiplicative functions "built"?

9. Two circles with diameter 1 are tangent to a line, as well as to each other. What is the diameter of the gray circle that is tangent to both circles as well as the line?

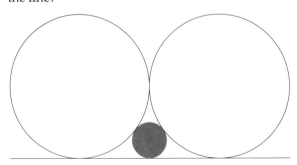

10. Start with the diagram from the previous problem, and add one more circle in the hole in the lower

left; it is also tangent to the line and two other circles. What is the diameter of this circle (marked in gray below)?

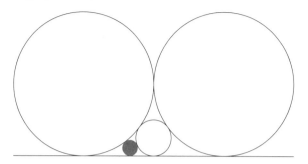

11. The function $k_5(n)$ counts the number of solutions to the equation $xy = 5 \bmod n$. Here's a table of the k_5 function for $1 \leqslant n \leqslant 24$.

n	1	2	3	4	5	6	7	8	9	10	11	12
$k_5(n)$	1	1	2	2	9	2	6	4	6	9	10	4

n	13	14	15	16	17	18	19	20	21	22	23	24
$k_5(n)$	12	6	18	8	16	6	18	18	12	10	22	8

Find a rule for the *child* of k_5.

12. Prove that if a and n are relatively prime, then there is a solution to the equation $ab = k$ in mod n for every number k from 0 to $n - 1$.

> One possible method: use a "pigeonhole" argument. What would happen if one of the equations couldn't be solved? Use that to find a contradiction.

13. Find all solutions to each of the following equations.

   a. $x^2 = 1$ in mod 3   **b.** $x^4 = 1$ in mod 5
   c. $x^6 = 1$ in mod 7   **d.** $x^{10} = 1$ in mod 11
   e. $x^5 = 1$ in mod 6

14. Let p be a prime. If $x^2 = 1$ in mod p, what are the possible values of x? Test some different mods to see what happens.

15. In mod 11, the perfect squares are 1, 4, 9, 5, and 3. Find all the perfect squares in each of these mods.

   a. mod 7   **b.** mod 13
   c. mod 17   **d.** mod 19

> Why write the perfect squares in this order? How were these found?

16. Find all solutions to each of the following equations.

   a. $x^3 = 1$ in mod 7   **b.** $x^3 = -1$ in mod 7
   c. $x^6 = 1$ in mod 13   **d.** $x^8 = 1$ in mod 17
   e. $x^9 = 1$ in mod 19

17. Without technology, find all the solutions to the equation $x^2 - 4x + 3 = 0$ in mod 165.

   Think about how you might handle this problem without enumerating all of mod 165.

18. Let $c(n)$ be the number of solutions to the equation $x^2 = 1$ in mod n. Prove that c is multiplicative.

Tough Stuff

19. Determine the grandparent of $m(n) = 1$.

20. Problem 11 involved a function called $k_5(n)$ and asked you to find a rule for its child. Find a more general rule for the child of $k_a(n)$, the number of solutions to the equation $xy = a$ in mod n. This rule should work for $a = 0$ and $a = 1$, among others.

21. Let $S = 1 + \frac{1}{3} + \frac{1}{5} + \frac{1}{7} + \cdots$ be the sum of the reciprocals of all odd numbers. Determine, with proof, whether this sum converges or diverges.

   A sum *diverges* if the sum eventually get larger than any real number. Some say it "goes to infinity" but that isn't really accurate.

22. Let $S = \frac{1}{2} + \frac{1}{3} + \frac{1}{5} + \frac{1}{7} + \cdots$ be the sum of the reciprocals of all prime numbers. Determine, with proof, whether this sum converges or diverges.

23. Let $S = 1 + \frac{1}{2} + \frac{1}{4} + \frac{1}{5} + \cdots + \frac{1}{12} + \frac{1}{14} + \cdots$ be the sum of the reciprocals of all numbers *that don't have a 3 in them*. Determine, with proof, whether this sum converges or diverges.

24. Find an odd number such that $\sigma(n) = 2n$, or prove that no such number exists.

Problem Set 6

Opener

Earlier problem sets defined the *child* of a function. The general rule is that

$$\text{child}(n) = \text{parent(all divisors of } n) \text{ added together}$$

Consider $m(n) = 1$. It's a function that always gives you the number 1. It is not a particularly interesting function, but it has an interesting family!

What is $m(7)$? What is $m(m(7))$? You get the idea.

Let t be the child of m and let u be the child of t. This means that

$$t(n) = m\text{(all divisors of } n) \text{ added together}$$
$$u(n) = t\text{(all divisors of } n) \text{ added together}$$
$$t(1) = m(1) = 1$$
$$t(15) = m(1) + m(3) + m(5) + m(15) = 4$$
$$u(16) = t(1) + t(2) + t(4) + t(8) + t(16) = ??$$

Fill in this table with the values of $t(n)$ and $u(n)$.

n	1	2	3	4	5	6	7	8	9	10	11	12
$m(n)$	1											
$t(n)$	1											
$u(n)$	1											

n	13	14	15	16	17	18	19	20	21	22	23	24
$m(n)$												
$t(n)$			4									
$u(n)$												

Important Stuff

1. Is t multiplicative? How about u? m?

2. You may have noticed primes play a large role in determining the values of the m, t, and u functions. Complete this shorter table for each function. Here, p is any prime.

A function is *multiplicative* if $f(ab) = f(a) \cdot f(b)$ whenever a and b don't have a common factor greater than 1.

n	m(n)	t(n)	u(n)
1			
p			
p^2			
p^3			
p^4			

3. Compute $m(420)$, $t(420)$, and $u(420)$ quickly, and without technology.

4.   **a.** If n is one more than a multiple of 3 and one more than a multiple of 8, what's the most you can say about the value of n?
   b. If n is 2 more than a multiple of 3 and 7 more than a multiple of 8, what's the most you can say about the value of n?

5. Many perfect squares are one more than a multiple of 24. For what values of n, from $1 \leqslant n \leqslant 48$, is n^2 one more than a multiple of 24?

6. Find all solutions to each of the following.
   a. $x^2 = 1$ in mod 3   **b.** $x^2 = 1$ in mod 8
   c. $x^2 = 1$ in mod 24   **d.** $x^2 = 1$ in mod 72

7. In Problem Set 5 you worked with the ϕ function, which counts how many numbers between 1 and n have no common factors with n (larger than 1). For example, $\phi(15) = 8$ because the numbers 1, 2, 4, 7, 8, 11, 13, and 14 all have no common factors with 15. (Note that $\phi(1) = 1$, not 0.)
   a. List all the numbers that make up $\phi(1)$, $\phi(3)$, $\phi(7)$, and $\phi(21)$.
   b. What is $\phi(1) + \phi(3) + \phi(7) + \phi(21)$?
   c. Simplify this expression as much as possible:

   $$1 + (p - 1) + (q - 1) + (p - 1)(q - 1)$$

Neat Stuff

8. Complete this table for some functions seen in previous problem sets. $\sigma(n)$ is the sum of the factors of n, $a(n) = \frac{\sigma(n)}{n}$, and $\phi(n)$ is given in Problem 7.

Answers here are in terms of p, so you might consider testing some different choices of p first. But not $p = 4$…

n	$\sigma(n)$	$a(n)$	$\phi(n)$
1			
p			
p^2			
p^3			
p^4			

9. If v is the child of u, what would its column in the table from Problem 2 look like? Compute $v(420)$.

10.   a. If x is 1 mod 3, 0 mod 5, and 0 mod 7, what is it in mod 105?
      b. If y is 0 mod 3, 1 mod 5, and 0 mod 7, what is it in mod 105?
      c. If z is 0 mod 3, 0 mod 5, and 1 mod 7, what is it in mod 105?
      d. Compute $2x + 3y + 4z$ in mod 105.

11. If x is 2 mod 3, 3 mod 5, and 4 mod 7, what is it in mod 105?

12. Find all solutions to each of the following. Try not to use a calculator.
    a. $x^2 = 1$ in mod 3   **b.** $x^2 = 1$ in mod 5
    c. $x^2 = 1$ in mod 7   **d.** $x^2 = 1$ in mod 15
    e. $x^2 = 1$ in mod 21   **f.** $x^2 = 1$ in mod 35
    g. $x^2 = 1$ in mod 105   **h.** $x^2 = 1$ in mod 420

13. Find all solutions to each of the following. A calculator should not be necessary.
    a. $x^2 = 2$ in mod 3   **b.** $x^2 = 2$ in mod 7
    c. $x^2 = 2$ in mod 17   **d.** $x^2 = 2$ in mod 21
    e. $x^2 = 2$ in mod 51   **f.** $x^2 = 2$ in mod 119
    g. $x^2 = 2$ in mod 357... which is $3 \times 7 \times 17$

The result in part (a) is very helpful in some later parts.

14. Prove that if f is multiplicative, then either $f(1) = 1$ or $f(n) = 0$ all the time.

15. Prove that if f and g are multiplicative functions, then $h = fg$, the product, is also multiplicative.

16. Find a value of n for which $x^2 = 2$ has exactly 8 solutions in mod n.

17. Define $c(x) = \frac{\phi(x)}{x}$.
    a. Explain why $c(x) < 1$ as long as $x > 1$.
    b. Find a value for which $c(x) < 0.1$ or show there is no such x.
    c. Find the minimum possible value of $c(x)$.

18. **a.** Find the parent of $m(n) = 1$; that is, find a function d so that m is the child of d.

   b. Find z, the parent of d.

19. Prove that if f is multiplicative, then so is $\frac{1}{f}$, the reciprocal, as long as $f(n) \neq 0$ for any n.

20. Find a rule or give a formula for each function.

   a. $f(m)$ is the number of solutions to $x^2 = x$ in mod m.

   b. $g_1(m)$ is the number of solutions to $xy = 1$ in mod m.

   c. $g_2(m)$ is the number of solutions to $x^2 - y^2 = 1$ in mod m.

   d. $h_1(m)$ is the number of solutions to $x^2 - y^2 = 0$ in mod m.

   e. $h_2(m)$ is the number of solutions to $x^2 + y^2 = 0$ in mod m.

Tough Stuff

21. Under what conditions is 2 a perfect square in mod m? Be careful about composite m…

22. Can a nonzero multiplicative function be its own ancestor (allowing for more than one generation)?

23. Let $s_4(n)$ be the number of ways to write n as the sum of four squares: $n = a^2 + b^2 + c^2 + d^2$ where a, b, c, d are integers (perhaps zero or negative). Starting with $s_4(1) = 8$, tabulate s_4 from 1 to 24. Is s_4 multiplicative? Fix it!

Problem Set 7

Opener

Consider the equation $x^2 = 2x$. On the array of numbers from 0 to 59 below:

1. Draw a circle around all of the numbers that are solutions to $x^2 = 2x$ in mod 5. That means if you circled 2, you should also circle 7, 12, 17...

   Instead of using circles and X's, you could also use colored markers.

2. Draw an X through all of the numbers that are solutions to $x^2 = 2x$ in mod 12. That means if you X'ed 2, you should also X 14, 26...

3. Find all solutions to $x^2 = 2x$ in mod 60.

0	1	2	3	4	5	6	7	8	9	10	11
12	13	14	15	16	17	18	19	20	21	22	23
24	25	26	27	28	29	30	31	32	33	34	35
36	37	38	39	40	41	42	43	44	45	46	47
48	49	50	51	52	53	54	55	56	57	58	59

Let $f(n)$ be the number of solutions to your equation in mod n, remembering that the actual numbers in mod n go from 0 to $n - 1$. What is $f(5)$? What is $f(12)$? What is $f(60)$?

Make sure $f(5)$ isn't larger than 5...

Important Stuff

1. A number is 3 more than a multiple of 5, and 7 more than a multiple of 12. Find some possible values of this number.

2. $\phi(n)$ counts the number of values between 1 and n that are relatively prime to n.

   a. What is $\phi(5)$? What is $\phi(12)$?

   b. If a number shares no common factors with 5 *and* no common factors with 12, what can you say about it?

   Two numbers are relatively prime *if they share no common factors greater than 1. It's just a quick way of saying that longer phrase.*

    c. Use the method from this set's Opener, or the method presented in Problem Set 6, to find all the numbers that are relatively prime to 60. The table below may be helpful.

1	2	3	4	5	6	7	8	9	10	11	12
13	14	15	16	17	18	19	20	21	22	23	24
25	26	27	28	29	30	31	32	33	34	35	36
37	38	39	40	41	42	43	44	45	46	47	48
49	50	51	52	53	54	55	56	57	58	59	60

    d. What is $\phi(60)$?

3. Let $P(n)$ be defined as the number of solutions to $xy = 1$ in mod n. What is $P(5)$? What is $P(12)$? What is $P(60)$?

Tracking down all the solutions making up $P(60)$ might take a while. Try to find a faster way.

4. The figure below shows two circles with diameter 1 that are tangent to the x-axis and mutually tangent at the point $\left(\frac{1}{2}, \frac{1}{2}\right)$. Two smaller circles are packed in as shown so they are tangent to the axis and the other circles. Use the overlaid grid on the handout at the end of this Problem Set to find the diameters and the coordinates of the centers of each of these smaller circles.

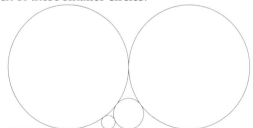

5. Fill in these two grids; one is the set of all possible sums when rolling two dice, and the other is the piece-by-piece expansion of $(x + x^2 + x^3 + x^4 + x^5 + x^6)^2$.

+	1	2	3	4	5	6
1						
2		5				
3						
4						
5		7				
6						12

$\times$	x	x^2	x^3	x^4	x^5	x^6
x						
x^2			x^5			
x^3						
x^4						
x^5		x^7				
x^6						x^{12}

    What do you notice?

6. Use technology to build a histogram for the number of ways (or, if you prefer, the probability) to roll each possible sum with four dice, from 4 to 24.

On TI-Nspire CAS, get a calculator screen (HOME icon), define $p(x)$ to be some specific interesting polynomial ("define $p(x) = \cdots$"), then tell the calculator:
$$\text{expand}(p(x)^4)$$

Neat Stuff

7. Define $c(n) = \frac{\phi(n)}{n}$.

   a. Make a table for c from 1 to 36, using exact fractional answers.
   b. Complete this table for $c(n)$ looking at powers of primes.

n	c(n)
1	
p	
p^2	
p^3	
p^4	

   c. Do you think it is possible for $c(n)$ to be less than 0.1? Explain.

8. Let $d(n) = a(n) \cdot c(n)$, where $a(n)$ is the sum of the reciprocals of the factors of n (introduced in Problem Set 2) and $c(n)$ is defined in Problem 7 above.

   a. Compute $d(n)$ from 1 to 36, giving decimal answers to four places.
   b. Does d seem to be multiplicative?
   c. Does d seem to have a maximum value? A minimum?

9. Solve these equations. The method of this set's Opener may be helpful.

   a. $x^2 + x = 2$ in mod 3   b. $x^2 + x = 2$ in mod 5
   c. $x^2 + x = 2$ in mod 7   d. $x^2 + x = 2$ in mod 15
   e. $x^2 + x = 2$ in mod 21   f. $x^2 + x = 2$ in mod 35
   g. $x^2 + x = 2$ in mod 105

10. a. If x is 1 mod 3, 0 mod 5, and 0 mod 11, what is it in mod 165?
    b. If y is 0 mod 3, 1 mod 5, and 0 mod 11, what is it in mod 165?
    c. If z is 0 mod 3, 0 mod 5, and 1 mod 11, what is it in mod 165?
    d. Compute $2x + 4y + 8z$, answering in mod 165.

11. If x is 2 mod 3, 4 mod 5, and 8 mod 11, what is it in mod 165?

12. How many solutions are there to $x^2 = 1$ in mod 165?

13. Which of the following functions are multiplicative?

    a. $b(n) = \frac{1}{n}$

    b. $\sigma_2(n)$, the sum of the squares of the divisors of n

    c. $\chi(n) = \begin{cases} 1 & \text{if } n = 4k+1 \text{ for some positive integer } k \\ -1 & \text{if } n = 4k-1 \text{ for some positive integer } k \\ 0 & \text{if } n \text{ is even} \end{cases}$

14. Katya says that you can identify a multiplicative function just by declaring what it does to powers of primes. For each description, give a simple rule for the function f.

    a. $f(p^k) = k+1$
    b. $f(p^k) = 1$
    c. $f(p^k) = p^k$
    d. $f(p^k) = 1 + p + p^2 + \cdots + p^k$

15. In Problem Set 5 you observed that the child of the ϕ function is the identity function. For example:

    $$\phi(1) + \phi(3) + \phi(5) + \phi(15) = 15$$

    $$\phi(1) + \phi(2) + \phi(7) + \phi(14) = 14$$

    Prove that in general,

    $$\sum_{d|n} \phi(d) = n$$

    The notation $d|n$ means "d divides n", or that d is a factor of n. This allows summation to happen only for specific values of d instead of the usual 1, 2, 3, 4...

16. Two circles with diameter 1 are tangent to the x-axis, and mutually tangent at the point $(\frac{1}{2}, \frac{1}{2})$. A series of smaller circles are packed in as shown below so they are tangent to the axis and the other circles. Determine the diameters and the coordinates of the centers of each of these smaller circles.

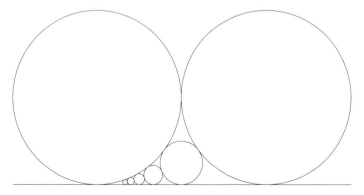

17. Let $a(n)$ be the sum of the reciprocals of the factors of n. Find a simple rule for the *parent* of this function.

How is a defined? Does this help you find the parent more easily?

18. a. Find the parent of $m(n) = 1$; that is, a function d so that m is the child of d.
   b. Find z, the parent of d.
   c. Describe a general method to find the parent of any multiplicative function.

19. Find the smallest value of $k > 0$ so that each equation has the *maximum possible* number of solutions.
   a. $x^k = 1$ in mod 5
   b. $x^k = 1$ in mod 15
   c. $x^k = 1$ in mod 105

Tough Stuff

20. Find the minimum possible value of $d(n)$, where d is the function from Problem 8.

21. Find the maximum possible value of $b(n)$, the sum of the reciprocals of the squares of the divisors of n.

22. Prove that a function is multiplicative if and only if its child is multiplicative.

Handout — Problem Set 7

The two largest circles have diameter 1. What are the diameters and the x-coordinates of the smaller circles?

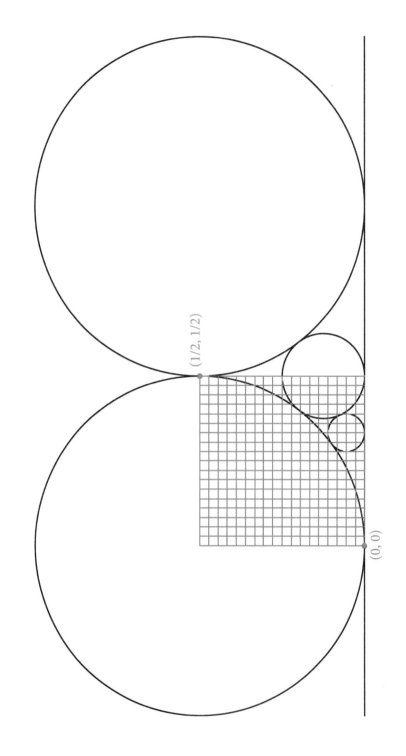

(1/2, 1/2)

(0, 0)

Problem Set 8

Opener

The following steps can be used to find all solutions to $x^3 - 1 = 0$ in mod 63:

- Find all solutions to $x^3 - 1 = 0$ in mod 7.

- Find all solutions to $x^3 - 1 = 0$ in mod 9.

- Use a grid technique to find all solutions in mod 63.

As in Problem Set 7, draw a circle around any solution to $x^3 - 1 = 0$ in mod 7 (and its equivalent numbers), and draw an X through any solution to $x^3 - 1 = 0$ in mod 9 (and its equivalent numbers).

0	1	2	3	4	5	6	7	8
9	10	11	12	13	14	15	16	17
18	19	20	21	22	23	24	25	26
27	28	29	30	31	32	33	34	35
36	37	38	39	40	41	42	43	44
45	46	47	48	49	50	51	52	53
54	55	56	57	58	59	60	61	62

If 4 solves $x^3 - 1 = 0$ in mod 7, you'd circle 4, 11, 18, 25... By the way, a number is a multiple of 9 whenever its digits add up to a multiple of 9.

Let $f(n)$ be the number of solutions to your equation in mod n, remembering that the actual numbers in mod n go from 0 to $n-1$. What is $f(7)$? What is $f(9)$? What is $f(63)$?

Make sure $f(7)$ isn't larger than 7...

Important Stuff

1. a. If a number is a multiple of 63, is it *required* to be both a multiple of 7 and a multiple of 9?
    b. If a number is both a multiple of 7 and a multiple of 9, is it *required* to be a multiple of 63?

2. a. If a number is a multiple of 60, is it *required* to be both a multiple of 6 and a multiple of 10?
    b. If a number is both a multiple of 6 and a multiple of 10, is it *required* to be a multiple of 60?

3. If you didn't get the chance to do Problem Set 7's circle problem, try it now. Use the grid (counting boxes) to find the diameters and centers of the two smaller circles.

Each box is $\frac{1}{36}$ on a side.

4. A formula for dealing with Problem Set 7's circle problem was discovered by Descartes, forgotten, then rediscovered in Japan in the early 19th Century.

   Suppose three circles are all mutually tangent, and tangent to the same line. If the *reciprocals* of the circles' diameters are a, b, c then, amazingly,

   $$2(a^2 + b^2 + c^2) = (a + b + c)^2$$

   a. Let $a = 1$ and $b = 1$. Use the equation above to find both possible values of c.
   b. Use c to determine the diameter of the first small circle.
   c. Let $a = 1$ and $b = 4$. Use the equation to find both possible values of c.
   d. Find the diameter of the second small circle.
   e. Find the diameter of the third small circle. (What should a and b equal?)
   f. Find the diameter of the fourth small circle, and the fifth.

   Don't forget: these are the reciprocals. A formula using the actual diameters can be written, but it's not as clean.

   Wait, in part (b) there are two values of c. What does the other value of c give for the diameter? What would a circle with that diameter look like?

5. Look back at Problem Set 7's set and work through Problems 5 and 6 if you haven't already.

6. A rock-paper-scissors player makes their selection randomly. In five games, they picked paper once, rock three times, and scissors once. In how many different ways could this have happened?

   One way is PRRRS, another is RPRSR.

7. With a computer algebra system, find the expansion of $(p+r+s)^5$ and use it to answer the previous question.

Neat Stuff

8. **a.** If x is 1 in mod 7 and 0 in mod 9, what is it in mod 63?
   b. If y is 0 in mod 7 and 1 in mod 9, what is it in mod 63?
   c. Compute the following nine quantities, giving answers in mod 63:

$x + y$	$2x + y$	$4x + y$
$x + 4y$	$2x + 4y$	$4x + 4y$
$x + 7y$	$2x + 7y$	$4x + 7y$

   Compare to this set's Opener. What do you notice?

9. Describe a method to solve *any* equation in mod 63.

10. Describe a method to predict the number of solutions to any equation in mod 63.

11. Solve $x^2 + x = 6$ in mod 105.

12. How many solutions are there to $x^2 = 1$ in mod 1155?

What is the prime factorization of 1155?

13. Complete this table for $\phi(n)$ and its child.

Remember, the *child* of a function is found by adding its divisors' outputs. For example, $s(27) = \phi(1) + \phi(3) + \phi(9) + \phi(27)$.

n	$\phi(n)$	$s(n)$
1	1	1
p		
p^2		
p^3		
p^4		

14. Use geometric reasoning, rather than the algebraic formula given earlier, to find the diameter of a circle placed in the "gap" between two circles of diameter $\frac{1}{a}$ and $\frac{1}{b}$.

The ending rule is simpler using $\frac{1}{a}$ and $\frac{1}{b}$, but you might prefer to use other variables in the short term.

15. Consider a set of circles like the ones in Problem 3, but an infinite number of them. Give an argument that states that the total area of *all* these circles is finite.

16. Find all solutions to each of the following.

    a. $x^4 = 1$ in mod 5   **b.** $x^6 = 1$ in mod 7
    c. $x^{24} = 1$ in mod 35   **d.** $x^8 = 1$ in mod 15

17. Let $f(n) = 1$ if n can be written as the sum of two squares, and $f(n) = 0$ if it can't be done.

    a. Tabulate f from 1 to 24.
    b. Is f multiplicative?
    c. How does the child of f behave?

18. Let $f(n) = 1$ if n is a perfect square mod 63, and 0 if not. Is f multiplicative?

Tough Stuff

19. Use the circles from this set's problems to say something interesting about the infinite sum

$$1 + \frac{1}{4} + \frac{1}{9} + \frac{1}{16} + \frac{1}{25} + \cdots$$

20. Relate the previous problem to the behavior of function d from Problem 8 from Problem Set 7.

21. This identity shows that if m and n can be written as the sum of two squares, then mn can be written as the sum of two squares:

$$(a^2 + b^2)(c^2 + d^2) = (ac - bd)^2 + (ad + bc)^2$$

Find an identity that shows the same fact when m and n are each written as the sum of four squares.

Believe it or not, knowledge of quaternions can be helpful here. It is not required, though.

Problem Set 9

Opener

The table below contains the numbers from 0 to 69 arranged so that their remainders after dividing by 7 and 10 are shown in the first column or last row. The numbers from 0 to 10 have already been filled in for you. Fill in the rest of the numbers.

number mod 7										
6							6			
5						5				
4					4					
3	10			3						
2			2							9
1		1							8	
0	0							7		
	0	1	2	3	4	5	6	7	8	9

number mod 10

As an example in the grid, the number 10 is 0 mod 10, and it's 3 mod 7, so it shows up with "coordinates" (0,3). Where should 11 be placed next?

Important Stuff

1. **a.** Find all solutions to $x^2 - x - 2 = 0$ in mod 7.
   b. Find all solutions to $x^2 - x - 2 = 0$ in mod 10.
   c. Use the table in the box above and your answers in mod 7 and mod 10 to quickly find all eight solutions to $x^2 - x - 2 = 0$ in mod 70.

2. Try making a chart like the one above, using mod 6 and mod 10 instead. What happens when you try to fill in this chart with numbers from 0 to 59?

3. On the handout at the end of this Problem Set, a path has been drawn from the edge of the largest circle on the right through all the tiny circles. *All* of them, an infinite number... The path is straight between centers of consecutive circles.

   a. How long is the piece of the path that goes through the first small circle (in the center of the diagram)?

   b. How long is the piece of the path that goes through the second small circle?

   c. Write an expression for the total length of the path, including the diameter running through the largest circle on the right.

4. A curved path goes from point A to point B, then point C, then point D. Timon decides to walk in a straight line from A to B, then B to C, then C to D. Is Timon's walk longer or shorter than the path? Always? Explain in brief.

5. Function $b(n)$ gives the sum of the reciprocals of the *squares* of the divisors of n. For example:

$$b(15) = 1 + \frac{1}{9} + \frac{1}{25} + \frac{1}{225}$$

The divisors of 15 are 1, 3, 5, and 15; so the denominators are $1^2, 3^2, 5^2$, and 15^2.

For each of these, write the entire list of fractions that make up $b(n)$ or the first k terms as listed.

   a. All terms of $b(10)$

   b. All terms of $b(6)$

   c. All terms of $b(24)$

   d. The first 6 terms of $b(60)$

   e. The first 10 terms of $b(2520)$

What's interesting about the number 2520?

6.   a. Complete this table, where $f(n)$ is the number of solutions to $x^2 = n$ over the integers. Many of the answers are zero.

$f(9) = 2$ because $9 = 3^2$ and $9 = (-3)^2$. Both 3 and -3 solve $x^2 = 9$.

n	0	1	2	3	4	5	6	7	8	9	10	11	12
$f(n)$	1		0							2			

n	13	14	15	16	17	18	19	20	21	22	23	24	25
$f(n)$	0												

   b. Is f multiplicative? Explain.

   c. Like the "dice polynomial" $x + x^2 + x^3 + x^4 + x^5 + x^6$, write a polynomial that expresses the number of different ways to write numbers as a perfect square. (This polynomial will include the term $2x^9 \ldots$)

For the purpose of this problem, stop at $2x^{25}$, but keep in mind that this polynomial actually goes on forever with higher-degree terms. This didn't happen with the dice polynomial, which stops at the x^6 term.

7. **a.** Either by hand or with technology, square the polynomial you found in Problem 6. Complete this table where $f_2(n)$ is the coefficient of x^n in the squared polynomial.

n	0	1	2	3	4	5	6	7	8	9	10	11	12
$f_2(n)$	1		4							4			

n	13	14	15	16	17	18	19	20	21	22	23	24	25
$f_2(n)$	8												

b. Is f_2 multiplicative? Explain.

8. **a.** Find the number of different ways to write 2 as the sum of two squares. Two such ways are $1^2 + (-1)^2$ and $(-1)^2 + 1^2$, but there are two more.

b. Find the number of different ways to write 7 as the sum of two squares.

c. How many different ways can you write 9 as the sum of two squares?

d. How many different ways can you write 13 as the sum of two squares?

e. How many different ways can you write 25 as the sum of two squares?

> Any differences count. For example, $2^2 + 1^2$, $(-2)^2 + 1^2$, and $1^2 + 2^2$ are all different ways to write 5 as the sum of two squares.

Neat Stuff

9. **a.** Use the chart from this set's Opener to find a, a number that is 1 in mod 10 and 0 in mod 7.

b. Find b, a number which is 0 in mod 10 and 1 in mod 7.

c. Calculate $4a + 6b$ in mod 70. Notice anything?

d. Calculate $7a + 2b$ in mod 70.

10. Here's an interesting circle packing situation. Start with the right-side circle with diameter 1 (labeled "1" in the diagram on the next page) and the circle of diameter $\frac{1}{4}$ from the usual diagram we've been using (labeled "2"). Now, stuff a tangent circle between those, to the right of the circle with diameter $\frac{1}{4}$. Remember, the formula to find the diameter of new circles is

$$2(a^2 + b^2 + c^2) = (a + b + c)^2$$

In this formula, a, b, c are the reciprocals of the circles' diameters.

> An article on circle packing written by a PCMI participant is available online at http://mathforum.org/ pcmi/hstp/resources/ circlepacking.

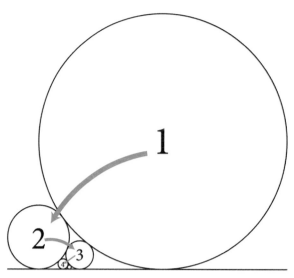

   a. What is this small circle's diameter? (It is labeled "3" above.)

   b. Now stuff another circle to the *left* of that (a tiny "4"). What is its diameter? Note: It's not $\frac{1}{16}$.

   c. Now stuff another circle to the *right* of that (a tinier "5"). What is its diameter?

   d. Now stuff another circle to the *left* of that (an even tinier "6"). What is its diameter?

   e. Notice anything?

11. Complete this table for $c(n) = \frac{\phi(n)}{n}$ and $a(n) = \frac{\sigma(n)}{n}$ along with $d(n) = c(n) \cdot a(n)$.

n	$c(n)$	$a(n)$	$d(n) = c(n)a(n)$
1	1	1	1
p	$1 - \dfrac{1}{p}$	$1 + \dfrac{1}{p}$	
p^2			
p^3			

12. Use what you know about the a function to show that for any $k > 0$, no matter how small, there is a value of n for which $c(n) < k$.

13. By hand, find all eight solutions to $x^2 = 3$ in mod 3289.

You'll need to know the factors of 3289 first. One factor is Michael Jordan's original jersey number.

14. The centers of the circles from Problem 10 are tending toward a specific point. Find its coordinates.

15. Find the number of different ways to write 25 as the sum of four squares. Three such ways are $0^2 + 0^2 + 5^2 + 0^2$, $3^2 + 0^2 + (-4)^2 + 0^2$, and $3^2 + (-4)^2 + 0^2 + 0^2$.

Do not write a computer program to do this – think! This question can be answered cleverly using other information from this problem set.

Tough Stuff

16. Let $p(x) = x + x^2 + x^3 + x^4 + x^5 + x^6 + \cdots$, like the dice polynomial, but it goes on forever.

    a. Let $p_2(x) = p(x)^2$, $p_3(x) = p(x)^3$, etc. Write the first few terms of $p_2(x)$, $p_3(x)$, and so forth, until you can describe to someone else what is happening. Then, instead of describing it, help them figure it out.

    b. Let $q_2(x) = \frac{x^2}{(1-x)^2}$, $q_3(x) = \frac{x^3}{(1-x)^3}$, etc. Find the 10th-degree Taylor polynomial expansion of $q_2(x)$, $q_3(x)$, and so forth, about $x = 0$. What do you notice?

17. You now have a method for generating the child of a function; describe a method for generating the parent.

18. Find a formula for the number of ways to write a number as the sum of two squares (including zero and negatives).

19. The triangular numbers are 0, 1, 3, 6, 10, 15, ... Can a number be written as the sum of two triangular numbers in more than one way? Find a formula for the number of ways to write a number as the sum of two triangular numbers.

20. Determine the end behavior of $d(n) = c(n)a(n)$. What are the maximum and minimum possible values for $d(n)$, and when do they occur?

As before, please try to think about this problem analytically—it can be and was done without a calculator or computer!

Handout — Problem Set 9
What is the length of the dotted path?

Problem Set 10

Opener

The function $b(n)$ returns the sum of the squares of the reciprocals of the factors of n. For example,

$$b(10) = 1 + \frac{1}{4} + \frac{1}{25} + \frac{1}{100}$$

since the factors of 10 are 1, 2, 5, and 10.

    a. Write out $b(4)$ as the sum of three numbers.

    b. Prove, beyond a reasonable doubt, that $b(4)$ is *less than* the total length of the path from Problem Set 9's handout (the dotted path on this problem set's handout).

    c. Write out $b(6)$ as the sum of four numbers.

    d. Again, prove that $b(6)$ is less than the total length of the dotted path.

    e. Write out $b(12)$ as the sum of six numbers. Is $b(12)$ less than the length of the dotted path?

    f. What about $b(60)$? $b(2520)$?

    g. Say, how long is that dotted path anyway? You were asked to write an expression for this in Problem Set 9.

    h. Justify this statement:

$$\text{For any } n, \; b(n) < 1 + \frac{1}{4} + \frac{1}{9} + \frac{1}{16} + \frac{1}{25} + \cdots.$$

Now, about that dotted path…

Important Stuff

    1. Consider the dashed path on this problem set's handout. Which is longer, the dotted path or the dashed path? Both paths start and end in the same place.

    2. Find the exact length of the dashed path.

    3. Prove that the length of the dotted path must be finite.

    4. Prove that there is a maximum possible value for $b(n)$.

    In an earlier problem set, we defined two seemingly different functions. We defined $P(n)$, which counts how many products xy are one more than a multiple of n, when x and y are allowed to range from 0 to n − 1. Then we defined φ(n), which counts how many numbers from 1 to n are relatively prime to n. Here are a few examples:

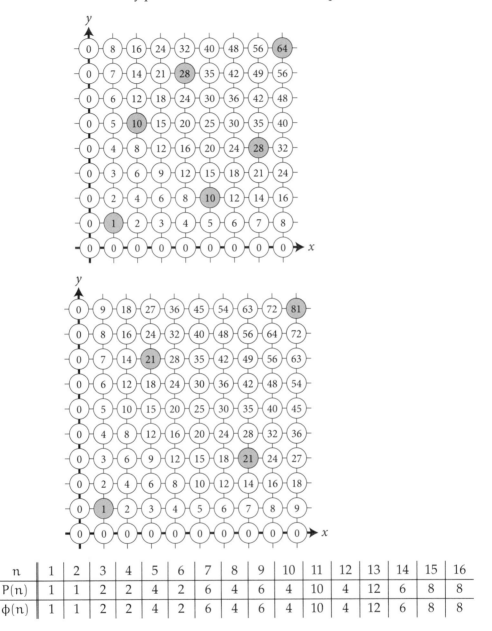

n	1	2	3	4	5	6	7	8	9	10	11	12	13	14	15	16
P(n)	1	1	2	2	4	2	6	4	6	4	10	4	12	6	8	8
φ(n)	1	1	2	2	4	2	6	4	6	4	10	4	12	6	8	8

The two functions appear to be identical.

5. **a.** Which numbers from 1 to 9 are relatively prime to 9?

   b. In which rows and columns do the products that contribute to P(9) appear?

Two numbers are *relatively prime* when they share no common factors greater than 1.

    c. Which numbers from 1 to 10 are relatively prime to 10?

    d. In which rows and columns do the products that contribute to P(10) appear?

6.   **a.** Find an n that equals 0 in mod 3, and 1 in mod 10.

    b. Find an n that equals 0 in mod 7, and 1 in mod 10.

    c. Find an n that equals 0 in mod 9, and 1 in mod 10.

7.   **a.** List all the numbers that make up $\phi(1), \phi(3), \phi(5)$, and $\phi(15)$.

    b. Multiply each set of numbers by $\frac{15}{n}$ where n is the input to each $\phi(n)$. For example, multiply all the elements of $\phi(5)$ by $\frac{15}{5} = 3$. What do you get?

> The elements of $\phi(5)$ are 1, 2, 3, 4; so the result for this piece would be 3, 6, 9, 12. The single element of $\phi(1)$ is 1.

    c. Repeat for 14 by looking at $\phi(1), \phi(2), \phi(7)$, and $\phi(14)$.

    d. Repeat for an interesting number of your choosing.

Neat Stuff

8. Below is a close-up of the tangent circles diagram, packed with all possible circles. Between each pair of tangent circles, stuff one tangent to them and to the x-axis. Continue this process forever, and you end up with an infinite number of circles that are all tangent to each other *and* the x-axis. The shaded regions are the two original circles with diameter 1.

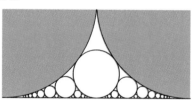

There is one circle with diameter $\dfrac{1}{2^2}$ and two circles with diameter $\dfrac{1}{3^2}$. What other circle diameters will you find, and how many of each size will you find?

9. Investigate a connection between the dotted path, the dashed path, and Pythagorean triples.

10. The centers of *all* the circles on the dotted path are on the same parabola. Find its equation, and sketch an accurate graph of the parabola on top of the circle diagram.

Remember it has to pass through all those centers!

11. Calculus (or a lookup table) can tell you the length of the parabola from Problem 10 from $x = 0$ to $x = 1$. Use the parabola to find a good upper bound for the sum

This isn't to say that the dashed path's upper bound isn't good, just that a better one can be found by using a parabola instead.

$$1 + \frac{1}{4} + \frac{1}{9} + \frac{1}{16} + \frac{1}{25} + \cdots$$

12. Find an upper bound for the total area of *all* the circles in Problem 8.

13. Explore the x-coordinates of the points of tangency of the circles in Problem 8. Specifically, if two neighboring circles are tangent at $x = \frac{a}{b}$ and $x = \frac{c}{d}$, what's the point of tangency of the stuffed-in circle?

14. Show that the left-and-right circles from Problem Set 9's set converge on an interesting point. Your work in Problem 13 may prove very helpful.

15. In Problem Set 9, you saw the power series $p(x) = 1 + 2x + 2x^4 + 2x^9 + 2x^{16} + \cdots$.

   a. Use a CAS or any other method to compute $(p(x))^4$ for powers of x 25 or less. Complete this table where $f_4(n)$ is the coefficient of x^n in the polynomial power.

Compare to the situation with four dice from a previous problem set. What would this fourth power represent?

n	0	1	2	3	4	5	6	7	8	9	10	11	12
$f_4(n)$													

n	13	14	15	16	17	18	19	20	21	22	23	24	25
$f_4(n)$													

   b. Show that f_4 is *not* multiplicative.
   c. Find a function related to f_4 that is multiplicative.
   d. What do you think $f_4(n)$ might be useful for?

16. Explore the relationship between $c_1(n) = \frac{n}{\phi(n)}$ and $a_1(n) = \frac{n}{\sigma(n)}$. This table may be helpful.

n	$c_1(n)$	$a_1(n)$	$c_1(n)a_1(n)$
1	1	1	1
p	$\frac{p}{p-1}$	$\frac{p}{p+1}$	
p^2			
p^3			

Tough Stuff

17. As n gets larger and larger, what happens to the value of $c_1(n)a_1(n)$? What happens to the value of the reciprocal, $c(n)a(n)$ from Problem Set 9?

18. Prove that

$$\sum_{n=1}^{\infty} \frac{\phi(n)}{n^4}$$

is finite.

19. Let c be a number between 0 and 1. Prove that c is irrational if and only if an *infinite* number of circles from the diagram in Problem 8 intersect the vertical line $x = c$.

Handout — Problem Set 10

What is the total length of the dashed path? How does it compare to the length of the dotted path?

Both paths start here and end at (0,0).

(1, 1/2)

(1, 0)

(0, 0)

Problem Set 11

Opener

You have now had some practice finding the child of a function. In Problem Set 6, you started with $m(n) = 1$ and found its child τ and grandchild u. Today, we're going the other way on m's family tree! Suppose m is the child of a function we'll call z. Then

$$m(n) = z(\text{all divisors of } n) \text{ added together}$$

Let's work it out, starting with $z(1)$. There's only one divisor, so $m(1) = z(1)$, and $z(1) = 1$. What about $z(2)$? Well...

$$\cancel{m(2)}^{\,1} = \cancel{z(1)}^{\,1} + z(2)$$

and $z(2) = 0$. Keep going with $z(3)$ and so on. Fill in the table with the values of z, the parent of m, and then the values of μ, the parent of z.

n	1	2	3	4	5	6	7	8	9	10	11	12	13	14	15
$\mu(n)$	1			0		1					1				
$z(n)$	1	0													
$m(n)$	1	1	1	1	1	1	1	1	1	1	1	1	1	1	1
$\tau(n)$	1	2	2	3	2	4	2	4	3	4	2	6	2	4	4
$u(n)$	1	3	3	6	3	9	3	10	6	9	3	18	3	9	9

n	16	17	18	19	20	21	22	23	24	25	26	27	28	29	30
$\mu(n)$															
$z(n)$									0						
$m(n)$	1	1	1	1	1	1	1	1	1	1	1	1	1	1	1
$\tau(n)$	5	2	6	2	6	4	4	2	8	3	4	4	6	2	8
$u(n)$	15	3	18	3	18	9	9	3	30	6	9	10	18	3	27

Careful when calculating $z(3)$, you only use the factors of 3:

$$m(3) = z(1) + z(3)$$

Similarly

$$m(4) = z(1)+z(2)+z(4)$$

Each time, fill in the ones you know... and there should only be one left! The greek letter μ is pronounced "mew".

You may feel negatively about some values you're getting for the μ function, but as long as the arithmetic works, it works.

1. Review your notes from Problem Sets 1–10 and write down five things that you thought were interesting, or things that you're still wondering about.

Important Stuff

For example, when you end up seeing a term like $\frac{1}{2^s 3^s}$, write that as $\frac{1}{6^s}$. But don't try to simplify something like $\frac{2}{2^s}$ to $\frac{1}{2^s-1}$, just leave it so the denominators are all k^s.

2. Find the first ten numerators in this product. Do not simplify. What does this have to do with this set's Opener?

$$\left(\frac{1}{1^s} + \frac{1}{2^s} + \frac{1}{3^s} + \frac{1}{4^s} + \cdots\right)^2 = \frac{?}{1^s} + \frac{?}{2^s} + \frac{?}{3^s} + \frac{?}{4^s} + \cdots$$

3. A function is *multiplicative* if $f(ab) = f(a) \cdot f(b)$ whenever a and b don't have a common factor greater than 1.

   a. If f is multiplicative, explain why $f(5) = f(1)f(5)$ must be true.

   b. Suppose $f(5)$ is nonzero. What does the above equation say about $f(1)$?

   c. If $f(1) > 1$, explain why f *cannot* be multiplicative.

4. Define $s_2(n)$ to be the number of ways to write n as the sum of two squares, where the order and signs of numbers matters. For example, $s_2(10) = 8$ because

$$10 = 3^2+1^2 = (-3)^2+1^2 = 3^2+(-1)^2 = (-3)^2+(-1)^2$$

$$10 = 1^2+3^2 = 1^2+(-3)^2 = (-1)^2+3^2 = (-1)^2+(-3)^2$$

The handout at the end of this Problem Set should be very helpful. What shape is formed by the eight 10s on this handout?

Fill in this table by using this problem set's handout.

n	0	1	2	3	4	5	6	7	8	9	10	11	12
$s_2(n)$	1		4								8		

n	13	14	15	16	17	18	19	20	21	22	23	24	25
$s_2(n)$	8												

5.   **a.** Determine whether s_2 is multiplicative.

    b. Let $S_2(n) = \frac{s_2(n)}{4}$. Does S_2 appear to be multiplicative?

6. Multiply this out:

$$(1 + 2x + 2x^4 + 2x^9 + 2x^{16} + 2x^{25})^2$$

and write the terms in increasing order of exponent (so you'll write $4x^2$ before $8x^{10}$). What do you notice?

7. Define $s_4(n)$ to be the number of ways to write n as the sum of four squares, where the order and signs of numbers matters. For example, $s_4(1) = 8$ because

$$1 = (\pm 1)^2 + 0^2 + 0^2 + 0^2$$
$$1 = 0^2 + (\pm 1)^2 + 0^2 + 0^2$$
$$1 = 0^2 + 0^2 + (\pm 1)^2 + 0^2$$
$$1 = 0^2 + 0^2 + 0^2 + (\pm 1)^2$$

n	0	1	2	3	4	5	6	7	8	9	10	11	12
$s_4(n)$	1	8	24	32	24	48	96	64	24	104	144	96	96

n	13	14	15	16	17	18	19	20	21	22	23	24	25
$s_4(n)$	112	192	192	24	144	312	160	144	256	288	192	96	248

   a. Determine whether s_4 is multiplicative.

   b. Define a function $S_4(n)$ based on $s_4(n)$ that you think is multiplicative, and test a few examples.

8. Here's an interesting figure.

This comes from Mathematics Magazine's "Proof Without Words" from October 2001.

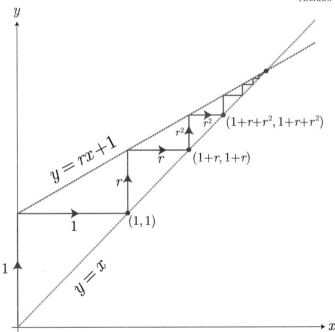

Where do the lines intersect, and what does this have to do with geometric series?

Neat Stuff

9. Find a rule that works for $\mu(n)$ for all the n in the table earlier, especially $n = 30$. For what numbers is $\mu(n) = 0$?

10. Write out a formula for the sum of an infinite geometric series.

11. Verify each of these formulas with one or two examples.

    a.
    $$1 + \frac{1}{x} + \frac{1}{x^2} + \cdots + \frac{1}{x^n} + \cdots = \frac{x}{x-1}$$

    b.
    $$1 + \frac{1}{x^2} + \frac{1}{x^4} + \cdots + \frac{1}{x^{2n}} + \cdots = \frac{x^2}{x^2 - 1}$$

    c.
    $$1 + r + r^2 + \cdots + r^n = \frac{1 - r^{n+1}}{1 - r}$$

12. Let p be any prime. Use this set's Opener to complete this table.

n	$\mu(n)$	$z(n)$	$m(n)$	$\tau(n)$	$u(n)$
1					
p					
p^2					
p^3					
p^4					

13. Multiply this out, again with selective cancellation (all terms should be in the form $\frac{n}{k^s}$). What does this have to do with this set's Opener?

$$\left(\frac{1}{1^s} + \frac{1}{2^s} + \frac{1}{3^s} + \frac{1}{4^s} + \cdots \right)^3 = \frac{?}{1^s} + \frac{?}{2^s} + \frac{?}{3^s} + \frac{?}{4^s} + \cdots$$

14. Multiply this out:

$$\left(\frac{1}{1^s} + \frac{1}{2^s} + \frac{1}{3^s} + \frac{1}{4^s} + \cdots \right)^0 = \frac{?}{1^s} + \frac{?}{2^s} + \frac{?}{3^s} + \frac{?}{4^s} + \cdots$$

15. Determine the unique set of coefficients that make the following equation true.

$$\left(\frac{1}{1^s} + \frac{1}{2^s} + \frac{1}{3^s} + \frac{1}{4^s} + \cdots \right) \left(\frac{?}{1^s} + \frac{?}{2^s} + \frac{?}{3^s} + \frac{?}{4^s} + \cdots \right) = 1$$

Use this diagram for the problems below. Remember, the shaded regions are the original circles, each with diameter 1.

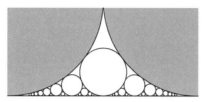

16. a. Show algebraically that if two tangent circles have diameters $\frac{1}{a^2}$ and $\frac{1}{b^2}$, the next stuff-it-inside circle will have diameter $\frac{1}{(a+b)^2}$.
   b. Show that if a and b are relatively prime, then so are a and $(a + b)$, and so are b and $(a + b)$.
   c. Prove that if two tangent circles in the diagram above have diameters $\frac{1}{a^2}$ and $\frac{1}{b^2}$, then a and b must be relatively prime.

17. Look for some Pythagorean triples in right triangles whose hypotenuses are the segments connecting the centers of mutually tangent circles. Can every primitive Pythagorean triple be found in this diagram eventually?

Tough Stuff

18. In the diagram above, a path goes from $(0,0)$ to $(1,0)$ through the centers of *all* the circles, in increasing order by x-coordinate. It zigzags a bit, but the length of the path through any one circle is always known. Is the total length of this path finite, or not? Find an upper bound or prove the path is infinitely long.

19. Prove that S_2 and S_4 are multiplicative. Try S_2 first; you may wish to use complex numbers a bit, since the norm of the Gaussian integer $a + bi$ is $a^2 + b^2$.

20. Consider a set of mutually tangent spheres on a plane. Find some relationships between the diameters of the mutually tangent spheres.

Handout — Problem Set 11

At each coordinate (x, y) is a circle containing the value $x^2 + y^2$.

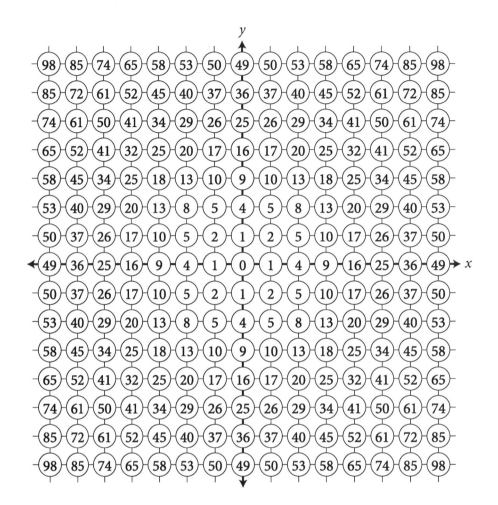

Problem Set 12

Opener

Recall the σ function from Problem Set 1, defined as the sum of the divisors of n. Let `id` be the parent of σ and `ego` be the grandparent of σ. Fill in this table, using what you learned previously about the parent-child connection.

n	1	2	3	4	5	6	7	8	9	10	11	12
ego(n)	1					2						
id(n)	1											
σ(n)	1	3	4	7	6	12	8	15	13	18	12	28

Important Stuff

1. Find the first ten numerators in this product of infinite sums. What does this have to do this set's Opener?

    As before, don't simplify terms like $\frac{2}{2^s}$ to $\frac{1}{2^{s-1}}$.

    $$\left(\frac{1}{1^s} + \frac{2}{2^s} + \frac{3}{3^s} + \frac{4}{4^s} + \cdots\right)\left(\frac{1}{1^s} + \frac{1}{2^s} + \frac{1}{3^s} + \frac{1}{4^s} + \cdots\right)$$

    $$= \frac{?}{1^s} + \frac{?}{2^s} + \frac{?}{3^s} + \frac{?}{4^s} + \cdots$$

2. Consider this infinite product of infinite sums:

    $$A = \left(1 + \frac{1}{2} + \frac{1}{4} + \frac{1}{8} + \cdots\right)$$
    $$\cdot \left(1 + \frac{1}{3} + \frac{1}{9} + \frac{1}{27} + \cdots\right)$$
    $$\cdot \left(1 + \frac{1}{5} + \frac{1}{25} + \frac{1}{5^3} + \cdots\right)$$
    $$\cdot \left(1 + \frac{1}{7} + \frac{1}{49} + \frac{1}{7^3} + \cdots\right) \cdots$$
    $$\cdot \left(1 + \frac{1}{p} + \frac{1}{p^2} + \frac{1}{p^3} + \cdots\right) \cdots$$

    This goes on forever. Let's *think* about what this expands to, but not actually carry out the expansion. The terms of the expansion come from picking one term from each set of parentheses, then multiplying them together. The final expansion is the sum of *all* such possibilities.

    a. Find a way to get $\frac{1}{12}$ by taking a piece from each factor.

    b. Is this the only way to get $\frac{1}{12}$?

    c. How many ways are there to get $\frac{1}{45}$?

    d. How many ways are there to get $\frac{1}{17}$?

    e. Pick another fraction in the form $\frac{1}{n}$ and describe how to get it in the expansion.

    f. What is the result of the expansion? How big is this product?

You've seen the result of this expansion sometime in the first four problem sets.

3. Consider this other infinite product of infinite sums:

$$
\begin{aligned}
B = &\left(1 + \frac{1}{4} + \frac{1}{16} + \frac{1}{4^3} + \cdots\right) \\
&\cdot \left(1 + \frac{1}{9} + \frac{1}{81} + \frac{1}{9^3} + \cdots\right) \\
&\cdot \left(1 + \frac{1}{25} + \frac{1}{25^2} + \frac{1}{25^3} + \cdots\right) \\
&\cdot \left(1 + \frac{1}{49} + \frac{1}{49^2} + \frac{1}{49^3} + \cdots\right) \cdots \\
&\cdot \left(1 + \frac{1}{p^2} + \frac{1}{p^4} + \frac{1}{p^6} + \cdots\right) \cdots
\end{aligned}
$$

This also goes on forever. So, what does it expand to? The same answer as the previous problem?

    a. Find a way to get $\frac{1}{144}$ by taking a piece from each factor.

    b. Is this the only way to get $\frac{1}{144}$?

    c. How many ways are there to get $\frac{1}{45^2}$?

    d. How many ways are there to get $\frac{1}{17^2}$?

    e. How many ways are there to get $\frac{1}{20}$? Why?

    f. Pick another fraction in the form $\frac{1}{n^2}$ and describe how to get it in the expansion.

    g. What is the result of the expansion? How big is this infinite product of infinite sums?

You've seen the result of this expansion sometime in the last four problem sets.

Recall the s_2 function, defined as the number of ways to write a number as the sum of two squares. The s_2 function isn't multiplicative since $s_2(1) = 4$, but $S_2(n) = s_2(n)/4$ seems to be multiplicative.

Turns out you can find a parent regardless of whether the original function is multiplicative. But, if the parent is multiplicative, the child is also multiplicative. Isn't the R_2 function amazing??

4. Let R_2 be the parent of S_2. Fill in this table with the values of $R_2(n)$.

n	1	2	3	4	5	6	7	8	9	10	11	12	13	14	15
$R_2(n)$	1		−1						1						
$S_2(n)$	1	1	0	1	2	0	0	1	1	2	0	0	2	0	0

n	16	17	18	19	20	21	22	23	24	25	26	27	28	29	30
$R_2(n)$															
$S_2(n)$	1	2	1	0	2	0	0	0	0	3	2	0	0	2	0

5. **a.** Write a simple rule that could be used to calculate $R_2(n)$ for any n.

b. Calculate this:

$$R_2(1)+R_2(2)+R_2(5)+R_2(10)+R_2(13)+R_2(26)+R_2(65)+R_2(130)$$

c. What is $S_2(130)$?

6. Using what you know about the R_2 function, find and justify a rule for $S_2(p)$ for prime p.

7. Find and justify a rule for $S_2(n)$ for any n. Your work in Problem 5 may help.

8. Suppose that f is a non-zero multiplicative function and g is its child. Let $f(3) = a$ and $f(7) = b$.

    a. What is the only possible value for $f(1)$?

    See Problem 3 from Problem Set 11.

    b. Calculate $f(21)$ in terms of a and b. Remember, f is multiplicative.

    c. Write $g(3)$ in terms of a. Remember, g is the child of f.

    The parent-child relationship means that $g(3) = f(1) + f(3)$.

    d. Write $g(7)$ in terms of b.

    e. Write $g(21)$ in terms of a and b.

    f. Is it true that $g(21) = g(3) \cdot g(7)$? For what kind of numbers could this argument be used?

Neat Stuff

9. Let p be any prime. Complete this table.

Among other greatest hits, this table uses the μ function from Problem Set 11, which is sometimes called the Möbius function.

n	$\sigma(n)$	$\mu(n)$	$\phi(n)$	$\tau(n)$
1				
p				
p^2				
p^3				
p^4				

10. A *lattice point* is a point with integer coordinates. How many lattice points are on the graph of each of these circles?

    a. $x^2 + y^2 = 25$
    b. $x^2 + y^2 = 65$
    c. $x^2 + y^2 = 1105$

11. Figure out the sequence of missing numerators. Can you do it without performing any algebra?

$$\left(\frac{?}{1^s} + \frac{?}{2^s} + \frac{?}{3^s} + \frac{?}{4^s} + \cdots\right)\left(\frac{1}{1^s} + \frac{1}{2^s} + \frac{1}{3^s} + \frac{1}{4^s} + \cdots\right)$$

$$= \frac{1}{1^s} + \frac{1}{2^s} + \frac{0}{3^s} + \frac{1}{4^s} + \frac{2}{5^s} + \frac{0}{6^s} + \frac{0}{7^s} + \frac{1}{8^s} + \frac{1}{9^s} + \frac{2}{10^s} + \frac{0}{11^s} + \frac{0}{12^s} + \cdots$$

12. Again, figure out the sequence of missing numerators. There is only one possible answer here.

$$\left(\frac{?}{1^s} + \frac{?}{2^s} + \frac{?}{3^s} + \frac{?}{4^s} + \cdots\right)\left(\frac{1}{1^s} + \frac{1}{2^s} + \frac{1}{3^s} + \frac{1}{4^s} + \cdots\right) = 1$$

13. Define $s_4(n)$ to be the number of ways to write n as the sum of four squares, where the order and signs of numbers matters. For example, $s_4(1) = 8$ because

Skip this problem if you answered it during Problem Set 11.

$$\begin{aligned}
1 &= (\pm1)^2 + 0^2 + 0^2 + 0^2 \\
1 &= 0^2 + (\pm1)^2 + 0^2 + 0^2 \\
1 &= 0^2 + 0^2 + (\pm1)^2 + 0^2 \\
1 &= 0^2 + 0^2 + 0^2 + (\pm1)^2
\end{aligned}$$

n	0	1	2	3	4	5	6	7	8	9	10	11	12
$s_4(n)$	1	8	24	32	24	48	96	64	24	104	144	96	96

n	13	14	15	16	17	18	19	20	21	22	23	24	25
$s_4(n)$	112	192	192	24	144	312	160	144	256	288	192	96	248

    a. Determine whether s_4 is multiplicative.

    b. Define a function S_4 based on s_4 that you think is multiplicative, and test a few examples.

14. Make a conjecture about the value of $S_4(p)$ for prime p.

15. Here's an interesting sequence of sequences.

Step	Sequence
1	1 1
2	1 2 1
3	1 3 2 3 1
4	1 4 3 2 3 4 1
5	1 5 4 3 5 2 5 3 4 5 1

At step n, look through the last sequence for two consecutive numbers that add to n, and whenever that happens, insert n. Investigate this and look for any interesting connections.

Try keeping track of the number of insertions. This might even connect with the tangent circles problem... In the next step, insert 6 anywhere two consecutive numbers add to 6.

16. Use the style of Problem 8 to prove more generally that if g is the child of f and f is multiplicative, then so is g.

Tough Stuff

17. Multiply this infinite product. What happens? Be specific! And prove it!

$$\left(1-\frac{1}{4}\right)\left(1-\frac{1}{9}\right)\left(1-\frac{1}{25}\right)\left(1-\frac{1}{49}\right)\cdots\left(1-\frac{1}{n^2}\right)\cdots$$

18. As with s_2 and s_4, define $s_3(n)$ as the number of ways to write n as the sum of *three* squares (with positions and signs of the three numbers being significant).

    a. Use a power series to help you generate data for s_3 quickly. Or, construct a three-dimensional version of Problem Set 11's handout...

    b. Is s_3 multiplicative or can it made multiplicative as with S_2 and S_4?

    c. Determine r_3, the parent of s_3. Notice anything?

19. Categorize all positive integers n that *cannot* be written as the sum of three squares.

20. Prove that any positive integer n can be written as the sum of four squares.

21. Find the exact value of each summation, or show that the sum diverges.

    a. $\displaystyle\sum_{n=1}^{\infty} \frac{1}{n^2}$ b. $\displaystyle\sum_{n=1}^{\infty} \frac{\sigma(n)}{n^2}$ c. $\displaystyle\sum_{n=1}^{\infty} \frac{\mu(n)}{n^2}$

    d. $\displaystyle\sum_{n=1}^{\infty} \frac{\phi(n)}{n^2}$ e. $\displaystyle\sum_{n=1}^{\infty} \frac{\tau(n)}{n^2}$

22. Define $s_m(n)$ to be the number of ways n can be written as the sum of m squares, where the order and signs of the numbers matters. For which positive integers m is s_m proportional to a multiplicative function?

Problem Set 13

Opener

If you haven't yet done it, use a CAS or any other method to expand this:
$$(1 + 2x^1 + 2x^4 + 2x^9 + 2x^{16} + \cdots)^4$$

The coefficient of the x^n term gives the number of ways n can be written as the sum of four squares, and is denoted by $s_4(n)$.

1. Determine $s_4(4)$.

2. Find all the ways to write 4 as the sum of four squares (you don't need to write them all out). Order and signs matter, so $(-1)^2 + (-1)^2 + 1^2 + 1^2$ is different from $1^2 + (-1)^2 + 1^2 + (-1)^2$.

3. Is s_4 multiplicative? Explain.

Let $S_4(n) = \frac{s_4(n)}{8}$ and let R_4 be the parent of S_4. Fill in this table with the values of $R_4(n)$.

n	1	2	3	4	5	6	7	8	9	10	11	12	13	14	15
$R_4(n)$	1			0	5										
$S_4(n)$	1	3	4	3	6	12	8	3	13	18	12	12	14	24	24

n	16	17	18	19	20	21	22	23	24	25	26	27	28	29	30
$R_4(n)$															
$S_4(n)$	3	18	39	20	18	32	36	24	12	31	42	40	24	30	72

Important Stuff

1. Compute the following product. Keep going until you notice what is happening.

$$\left(\frac{1}{1^s} + \frac{2}{2^s} + \frac{3}{3^s} + \frac{0}{4^s} + \frac{5}{5^s} + \frac{6}{6^s} + \frac{7}{7^s} + \frac{0}{8^s} + \frac{9}{9^s} + \cdots\right)\left(\frac{1}{1^s} + \frac{1}{2^s} + \frac{1}{3^s} + \frac{1}{4^s} + \cdots\right) = ??$$

2. Look back at the last few problem sets' expansion problems. Describe what happens when you multiply through by

$$\left(\frac{1}{1^s} + \frac{1}{2^s} + \frac{1}{3^s} + \frac{1}{4^s} + \cdots\right)$$

What form must the other expression have for this to work?

3. Check out this table of values of the Möbius μ function.

n	factorization of n	$\mu(n)$	n	factorization of n	$\mu(n)$
1	1	1	16	2^4	0
2	2	-1	18	$2 \cdot 3^2$	0
3	3	-1	20	$2^2 \cdot 5$	0
4	2^2	0	21	$3 \cdot 7$	1
5	5	-1	24	$2^3 \cdot 3$	0
6	$2 \cdot 3$	1	25	5^2	0
7	7	-1	30	$2 \cdot 3 \cdot 5$	-1
8	2^3	0	35	$5 \cdot 7$	1
9	3^2	0	36	$2^2 \cdot 3^2$	0
10	$2 \cdot 5$	1	60	$2^2 \cdot 3 \cdot 5$	0
11	11	-1	77	$7 \cdot 11$	1
12	$2^2 \cdot 3$	0	99	$3^2 \cdot 11$	0
14	$2 \cdot 7$	1	210	$2 \cdot 3 \cdot 5 \cdot 7$	1
15	$3 \cdot 5$	1	2310	$2 \cdot 3 \cdot 5 \cdot 7 \cdot 11$	-1

Use the table to write a rule to calculate $\mu(n)$ for any n. Use your rule to calculate $\mu(120)$, $\mu(5005)$ and $\mu(30030)$.

Your rule for μ can be a sentence or two, it doesn't have to contain complicated symbols.

4. Look back at the Opener from Problem Set 11, then figure out the sequence of missing numerators in this equation below. Try to do it without performing any algebra.

$$\left(\frac{?}{1^s} + \frac{?}{2^s} + \frac{?}{3^s} + \frac{?}{4^s} + \frac{?}{5^s} + \frac{?}{6^s} + \cdots\right)\left(\frac{1}{1^s} + \frac{1}{2^s} + \frac{1}{3^s} + \frac{1}{4^s} + \frac{1}{5^s} + \frac{1}{6^s} + \cdots\right)$$

$$= \frac{1}{1^s} + \frac{0}{2^s} + \frac{0}{3^s} + \frac{0}{4^s} + \cdots$$

5. Find the first six numerators in this product of infinite sums, and compare to this set's Opener.

$$\left(\frac{1}{1^s} + \frac{3}{2^s} + \frac{4}{3^s} + \frac{3}{4^s} + \frac{6}{5^s} + \frac{12}{6^s} + \cdots\right)\left(\frac{1}{1^s} + \frac{-1}{2^s} + \frac{-1}{3^s} + \frac{0}{4^s} + \frac{-1}{5^s} + \frac{1}{6^s} + \cdots\right)$$

$$= \frac{?}{1^s} + \frac{?}{2^s} + \frac{?}{3^s} + \frac{?}{4^s} + \frac{?}{5^s} + \frac{?}{6^s} + \cdots$$

6. Patty believes that

$$1 + \frac{1}{2^2} + \frac{1}{3^2} + \frac{1}{4^2} + \cdots = \left(1 + \frac{1}{4} + \frac{1}{16} + \frac{1}{4^3} + \cdots\right)$$
$$\cdot \left(1 + \frac{1}{9} + \frac{1}{81} + \frac{1}{9^3} + \cdots\right)$$
$$\cdot \left(1 + \frac{1}{25} + \frac{1}{25^2} + \frac{1}{25^3} + \cdots\right)$$
$$\cdot \left(1 + \frac{1}{49} + \frac{1}{49^2} + \frac{1}{49^3} + \cdots\right) \cdots$$
$$\cdot \left(1 + \frac{1}{p^2} + \frac{1}{p^4} + \frac{1}{p^6} + \cdots\right) \cdots$$

Is she right? Why or why not?

7. Here is another infinite product.

$$M = \left(1 - \frac{1}{2}\right)\left(1 - \frac{1}{3}\right)\left(1 - \frac{1}{5}\right)\left(1 - \frac{1}{7}\right) \cdots \left(1 - \frac{1}{p}\right) \cdots$$

   a. Will you find a $\frac{1}{15}$ term in this product? Why or why not? If so, what is its sign?
   b. Will you find a $\frac{1}{18}$ term in this product? Why or why not? If so, what is its sign?
   c. What's the sign of $\frac{1}{17}$?
   d. What happens with $\frac{1}{20}$? $\frac{1}{30}$? $\frac{1}{5005}$?
   e. What denominators do you get, and with what signs?
   f. What is the result of the expansion?

Neat Stuff

8. The last problem explored a product called M. Here is $\frac{1}{M}$:

$$\frac{1}{M} = \left(\frac{1}{1 - \frac{1}{2}}\right)\left(\frac{1}{1 - \frac{1}{3}}\right)\left(\frac{1}{1 - \frac{1}{5}}\right)\left(\frac{1}{1 - \frac{1}{7}}\right) \cdots$$

Take each term from the original product and push it into the denominator.

Hey…these are all in the form $\frac{1}{1-r}$, like sums of geometric series.

   a. Unravel each geometric series into its terms. For example, $\frac{1}{1-\frac{1}{2}} = 1 + \frac{1}{2} + \frac{1}{4} + \cdots$.
   b. Now multiply out the new $\frac{1}{M}$, if you haven't already.
   c. How big is $\frac{1}{M}$? What does that say about the value of M?

Look back at previous problem sets – you may have seen this before!

9. Repeat the last two problems with this infinite product:

This is pretty tough, but follow the steps you used in Problems 7 and 8.

$$N = \left(1 - \frac{1}{2^2}\right)\left(1 - \frac{1}{3^2}\right)\left(1 - \frac{1}{5^2}\right)\left(1 - \frac{1}{7^2}\right)\cdots\left(1 - \frac{1}{p^2}\right)\cdots$$

What does the expansion of N look like? Find the value of N as exactly as you can by exploring the geometric series buried inside $\frac{1}{N}$. There has to be a value, since N must be between 0 and 1...

10.   a. If two positive integers are picked at random, what is the probability that they are *both* multiples of 2?

   b. What is the probability that at least one of the two numbers *isn't* a multiple of 2? Psst: use $1 - p$.

   c. What is the probability that at least one of the two numbers *isn't* a multiple of 3?

   d. What is the probability that the two numbers don't have a common factor of 5? (This is the same as the last question.)

   e. What is the probability that the two numbers don't have a common factor of 7? of 11? of p for any prime?

   f. What is the probability that two positive integers picked at random won't have a common factor of 2, 3, *or* 5?

These are independent events.

   g. Write an expression for the probability that two positive integers picked at random will share *no* common factors.

11. What infinite series in the style of Problem 2 can be multiplied onto something to obtain its grandchild?

12. What infinite series in the style of Problem 2 can be multiplied onto something to obtain its grandparent?

13. Let p be any prime. Complete this table.

Answers may or may not be in terms of p.

n	ggp	gp	parent of m	m(n) = 1	child of m	gc	ggc
1							
p							
p^2							
p^3							
p^4							

14. Let p be any prime. Complete this table.

n	ggp	gp	parent of id	id(n) = n	child of id	gc	ggc
1							
p							
p^2							
p^3							
p^4							

15. Show that for any integer $n \geqslant 2$,

$$\phi(n) = n \prod_{p|n} \left(1 - \frac{1}{p}\right).$$

What do those symbols mean anyway?

16. Investigate the behavior of this function.

$$f(n) = \frac{\sum_{k=1}^{n} \phi(k)}{n^2}$$

Tough Stuff

17. Read a few proofs that show

$$1 + \frac{1}{4} + \frac{1}{9} + \frac{1}{16} + \cdots = \frac{\pi^2}{6}$$

18. Write a summation that is equal to $\frac{\pi^4}{36}$.

19. What is $\lim_{n \to \infty} \frac{1}{n^2} \sum_{k=1}^{n} s_4(k)$? Prove it.

20. Suppose you have an unlimited supply of beads with k different colors. How many distinct necklaces with length n can you make? Try to find a way to solve this problem using Möbius inversion.

If R and B are two colors (say, raw umber and burnt umber), RBRRR and RRBRR are not distinct necklaces since they are related by a circular shift.

21. Find a nice rule for $s_3(n)$, the number of ways to write n as the sum of three squares.

Problem Set 14

Opener

The s_2 function is a bit of a mess. It increases and decreases haphazardly; it's frequently zero; and when it's not zero it's almost always a multiple of 4. One way to deal with a bizarre function like s_2 is to compute a running average.

So, any way you like, compute the average value of $s_2(n)$ when

1. n goes from 1 to 25
2. n goes from 1 to 49
3. n goes from 1 to 75
4. n goes from 1 to 108

You may find a previous handout helpful.

Important Stuff

1. Briefly explain why the following equation is true.

$$1 + \frac{1}{2^s} + \frac{1}{3^s} + \frac{1}{4^s} + \cdots = \left(1 + \frac{1}{2^s} + \frac{1}{4^s} + \frac{1}{8^s} + \cdots\right)$$
$$\cdot \left(1 + \frac{1}{3^s} + \frac{1}{9^s} + \frac{1}{27^s} + \cdots\right)$$
$$\cdot \left(1 + \frac{1}{5^s} + \frac{1}{25^s} + \frac{1}{5^{3s}} + \cdots\right)$$
$$\cdot \left(1 + \frac{1}{7^s} + \frac{1}{7^{2s}} + \frac{1}{7^{3s}} + \cdots\right) \cdots$$
$$\cdot \left(1 + \frac{1}{p^s} + \frac{1}{p^{2s}} + \frac{1}{p^{3s}} + \cdots\right) \cdots$$

2. Each of the infinite sums above, like

$$1 + \frac{1}{2^s} + \frac{1}{4^s} + \frac{1}{8^s} + \cdots$$

   is a geometric series. Find the value of each geometric series. Rewrite the right side of the above equation as simply as you can.

3. Let $s = 1$ in the equation above. What happens? Use this to prove that there must be infinitely many prime numbers.

4. Calculate enough terms of this infinite product so that you can identify what the answer is.

$$\left(1 - \frac{1}{2^s}\right)\left(1 - \frac{1}{3^s}\right)\left(1 - \frac{1}{5^s}\right)\left(1 - \frac{1}{7^s}\right)\cdots\left(1 - \frac{1}{p^s}\right)\cdots$$

$$= \frac{?}{1^s} + \frac{?}{2^s} + \frac{?}{3^s} + \frac{?}{4^s} + \frac{?}{5^s} + \frac{?}{6^s} + \cdots$$

Be strategic about expansion; what kinds of terms will you get?

5. Multiply this out. What happens?

$$\left(\frac{1}{1^s} + \frac{-1}{2^s} + \frac{-1}{3^s} + \frac{0}{4^s} + \frac{-1}{5^s} + \frac{1}{6^s} + \cdots + \frac{\mu(n)}{n^2} + \cdots\right).$$

$$\left(\frac{1}{1^s} + \frac{1}{2^s} + \frac{1}{3^s} + \frac{1}{4^s} + \frac{1}{5^s} + \frac{1}{6^s} + \cdots + \frac{1}{n^2} + \cdots\right) = ??$$

6. Find the result of this product. Use the last two problems to help you.

$$\left(1 - \frac{1}{4}\right)\left(1 - \frac{1}{9}\right)\left(1 - \frac{1}{25}\right)\left(1 - \frac{1}{49}\right)\cdots\left(1 - \frac{1}{p^2}\right)\cdots$$

Neat Stuff

7. What does this equal? Give a justification.

$$\lim_{n \to \infty} \frac{\sum_{k=1}^{n} s_2(k)}{n}$$

8. Imagine two dice with an infinite number of sides, labeled 1, 2, 3, 4, ... Two of these presumably spherical dice are rolled, and a result is calculated: the greatest common divisor of the two numbers rolled.

   a. Try this a few times. Randomly pick ten pairs of five- or six-digit numbers, then calculate the greatest common divisor of each pair. Did anything surprising happen? *If working with others, compare to see what may be happening overall.*

   b. Explain why it's exactly 4 times more likely for the result to be 1 than for it to be 2.

   c. How many times more likely is it for the result to be 1 than 3?

   d. How many times more likely is it for the result to be 1 than 4?

   e. Find the exact probability that the result is 1.

9. Use a result from previous problem sets to prove that no positive integer can have more factors that are "3 mod 4" than factors that are "1 mod 4".

10. **a.** What's the formula for the area of a circle?
    b. What's the formula for the volume of a sphere?
    c. What's the formula for the hypervolume of a four-dimensional hypersphere?

Either use calculus or look this up. Easy choice! Hopefully the answer is surprising either way.

11. In this set's Opener you calculated the long-term average value of s_2. Try again with s_4, and see if you find anything interesting.

12. Here's a grid of n^2 fractions:

$$\begin{array}{cccccc} \frac{1}{1} & \frac{1}{2} & \frac{1}{3} & \cdots & \frac{1}{n} \\ \frac{2}{1} & \frac{2}{2} & \frac{2}{3} & \cdots & \frac{2}{n} \\ \vdots & \vdots & \vdots & & \vdots \\ \frac{n}{1} & \frac{n}{2} & \frac{n}{3} & \cdots & \frac{n}{n} \end{array}$$

As n grows, what proportion of the fractions are in lowest terms? $\frac{6}{5}$ is in lowest terms, but $\frac{6}{4}$ isn't.

13. Show that

$$\sum_{d\mid n} |\mu(d)| = 2^{\text{number of distinct primes dividing } n}$$

14. You are the first of three contestants on the "Showcase Showdown" of The Price is Right, and on your first spin you get 65 cents. The winner is the one closest to $1.00 without going over on two spins, and any player may stop after one spin. The wheel has 0.05 to 1.00 in increments of 5 cents. Are you more likely to win by spinning again and risking going over $1.00, or by staying on 65 cents? Rigorously defend your logic.

Tough Stuff

15. What does this infinite product equal?

$$\left(1+\frac{1}{4}\right)\left(1+\frac{1}{9}\right)\left(1+\frac{1}{25}\right)\left(1+\frac{1}{49}\right)\cdots\left(1+\frac{1}{p^2}\right)\cdots$$

16. Prove that no positive integer can have more factors that are "2 mod 3" than factors that are "1 mod 3". Generalize to other mods... if possible.

17. Find a way to generate all of the Pythagorean triples in which *the two leg lengths* are one away from each other. One example is 21, 20, 29.

18. Solve the continuous version of the "Showcase Showdown" problem above, where numbers are picked continuously from 0 to 1 instead of discretely by increments of 0.05. Find the cutoff number n where it's correct to stay (as the first player of three) when you get more than n on the first try, and to go again with less than n.

Problem Set 15

Opener

Review all of the problem sets and make note of what you learned and thought about during each set. Start with Problem Set 1. What were the three most interesting things you came across?

Here are some questions that may have come up for you during your work throughout the course. Explore any of these questions, any of your own questions not included here, or any problems from earlier sets that you haven't had time to work on previously.

Problem Sets 1–5

1. Name six multiplicative functions, and three non-multiplicative functions.

2. Find five numbers for which $\sigma(n) = 2n$, and research to determine the largest known such number.

3. Show that the sum of unit fractions with even denominators

$$\frac{1}{2} + \frac{1}{4} + \frac{1}{6} + \frac{1}{8} + \cdots$$

   must be infinite.

4. Show that the sum of unit fractions with *odd* denominators

$$1 + \frac{1}{3} + \frac{1}{5} + \frac{1}{7} + \cdots$$

   must be infinite.

5. Determine the value of $\phi(210)$ as easily as possible by hand.

6. Determine the value of

$$\phi(1) + \phi(5) + \phi(13) + \phi(65)$$

7. What is the child of the ϕ function?

Problem Sets 6–10

1. Find all solutions to $x^2 = 4$ in mod 145 using the factorization $145 = 5 \cdot 29$.

2. Find all solutions to $x^3 - x = 4$ in mod 170.

3. Complete this table giving numbers that have one answer in mod 12, and a second answer in mod 7.

number mod 7	0	1	2	3	4	5	6	7	8	9	10	11
6							6					
5	12					5						
4					4							11
3				3							10	
2			2							9		
1		1							8			
0	0						7					

number mod 12

  a. Use the table to find a, the smallest positive number that is 1 mod 12 and 0 mod 7. Find b, the smallest positive number that is 0 mod 12 and 1 mod 7.
  b. Calculate $5a + 3b$ in mod 84.
  c. Use the table to find the smallest positive number that is 5 mod 12 and 3 mod 7.

4. Consider m and n, relatively prime integers. Suppose a is 0 in mod m and 1 in mod n, and b is 1 in mod m and 0 in mod n. If $0 \leqslant a, b \leqslant mn$, show that $b = mn - a + 1$.

5. Here are some circles. Each circle is constructed so that the nth circle has diameter $\frac{1}{n}$. Find the total circumference and area of *all* the circles built this way.

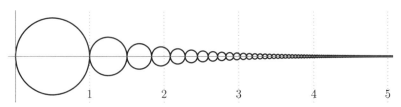

Problem Sets 11–14

1. In the Opener from Problem Set 14, as n increases, what happens to the average value of $s_2(n)$? How is this *physically* and/or geometrically related to the handout from Problem Set 11, which gave the $x^2 + y^2$ value at each location (x, y)?

2. Fill in the following table.

This squiggle is a Greek "zeta". $\zeta(s)$ is called the "Riemann zeta function".

$\zeta(s)^n$	Calculation	Result
$\zeta(s)^{-1}$		
$\zeta(s)^0$		
$\zeta(s)^1$	$\dfrac{1}{1^s} + \dfrac{1}{2^s} + \dfrac{1}{3^s} + \cdots$	$\dfrac{1}{1^s} + \dfrac{1}{2^s} + \dfrac{1}{3^s} + \dfrac{1}{4^s} + \cdots$
$\zeta(s)^2$	$\left(\dfrac{1}{1^s} + \dfrac{1}{2^s} + \dfrac{1}{3^s} + \cdots\right)^2$	$\dfrac{}{1^s} + \dfrac{}{2^s} + \dfrac{}{3^s} + \dfrac{}{4^s} + \cdots$
$\zeta(s)^3$		

Make a connection between what you see here and one of the Openers.

3. Given a function, how do you obtain the child? parent? grandchild? grandparent? Take a function and calculate its grandparent and grandchild functions, then multiply those together after writing them as $\frac{?}{1^s} + \frac{?}{2^s} + \cdots$. What happens?

4. How many lattice points are on the graph of $x^2 + y^2 = 3530$?

For Further Study...

1. The diagram below shows three circles of diameter 1, with a small circle in the middle.

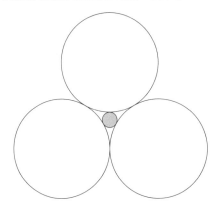

   Descartes found this formula relating the four diameters; as before, each variable is the *reciprocal* of the real diameter:

   $$(a + b + c + d)^2 = 2(a^2 + b^2 + c^2 + d^2)$$

   a. What is the diameter of the small circle?
   b. Now do it again, plopping yet another circle between the small circle and two of the big circles. What is its diameter?
   c. As more circles are plopped, what happens to their diameters? Do the diameters form a recognizable sequence?

   Amazing how simple this formula is, and how similar it is to the case of using a tangent line. What happens when you let $d = 0$? What would that circle look like?

2. You know that a multiplicative function satisfies $f(xy) = f(x)f(y)$, at least when x and y are relatively prime. Find a function for which each of these is true for any choices of the variables.

   a. $f(x + y) = f(x) + f(y)$
   b. $f(x + y) = f(x) \cdot f(y)$
   c. $f(xy) = f(x) + f(y)$
   d. $f(x + y) = (f(x))^y$

3. Given any integer $n > 2$, describe how to find a sequence of n consecutive *non*-primes. Does this contradict the earlier finding that there are an infinite number of primes?

4. Define a function λ that gives $\lambda(n) = 1$ if n has an even number of prime factors and $\lambda(n) = -1$ if n has an odd number of prime factors. This function takes into account the number of times that a prime factor is repeated. So, for example, $\lambda(1) = 1$ because 1 has zero prime factors,

$\lambda(2) = -1$ because 2 has one prime factor (namely, 2). The value of $\lambda(4) = 1$ because $4 = 2^2$ so it has the prime factor 2 appearing twice. Fill in this table with the values of λ, its child ν and its parent κ.

n	1	2	3	4	5	6	7	8	9	10	11	12	13	14	15
$\kappa(n)$	1														
$\lambda(n)$	1	-1	-1	1											
$\nu(n)$	1														

n	16	17	18	19	20	21	22	23	24	25	26	27	28	29	30
$\kappa(n)$	1														
$\lambda(n)$	1														
$\nu(n)$	1														

5. Prove or disprove: if a, b, c are positive integers and

$$(a + b + c + d)^2 = 2(a^2 + b^2 + c^2 + d^2)$$

then d must also be an integer. What does this imply about the circle packing diagram in Problem 1 above?

Tough Stuff

6. Define $f(n) = \sum_{k=1}^{n} \lambda(k)$. Is $f(n) \leqslant 0$ for all $n > 1$? Prove or find a counter-example.

7. Show that the following equation is true:

$$x\left(1 - \frac{x^2}{\pi^2}\right)\left(1 - \frac{x^2}{4\pi^2}\right)\left(1 - \frac{x^2}{9\pi^2}\right)\cdots = x - \frac{x^3}{6} + \frac{x^5}{120} - \frac{x^7}{7!} + \cdots$$

8. Calculate $\displaystyle\sum_{n=2}^{\infty} \sum_{m=1}^{n-1} \frac{1}{(mn)^2}$.

9. Calculate $\displaystyle\sum_{n=1}^{\infty} \sum_{m=1}^{\infty} \frac{1}{(mn)^2}$. It'll be related to $\frac{\pi^2}{6}$.

10. Use the previous two facts and a lovely grid to show that

$$\sum_{n=1}^{\infty} \frac{1}{n^4} = \frac{\pi^4}{90}$$

11. Use a similar setup to find the exact value of

$$\sum_{n=1}^{\infty} \frac{1}{n^6}.$$

CHAPTER

2

Facilitator Notes

The facilitator notes are designed to be used as needed. Each problem set has two components:

1. **Goals of the Problem Set** Here we lay out what the principal ideas of each problem set are.

2. **Notes on Selected Problems** We identify a few problems that are worth going over in a whole group discussion.

We will put our emphasis on the main goals of each lesson, drawn from the problems in the "Important Stuff."

Problem Set 1

Goals of the Problem Set

This course is about multiplicative functions, a concept that will be developed throughout the first few problem sets. Problem Set 1 is a study of one specific function, the σ ("sigma") function, that counts the sum of the divisors of an integer. Pattern recognition is a priority here, with the goal of emphasizing patterns that recur in many different functions.

Specifically, the σ function follows the rule that $\sigma(xy) = \sigma(x) \cdot \sigma(y)$ whenever x and y are relatively prime (share no common factors larger than 1). This fact may or may not emerge in Problem Set 1. As more multiplicative functions are presented, commonalities will emerge. There is no need to formalize any of the patterns participants discover at this time.

Problem Set 1 is also intended as an introduction to the style of the course. Consider having participants read the Introduction to learn about the course expectations.

Note that some participants may not get past Problem 1, and that's fine.

Notes on the Problems

The opener asks participants to complete the table without help from a calculator or computer, and we mean it! The table is deliberately too big for participants to blindly fill it in without using some sort of pattern or recognition of related answers. Here are some conjectures participants may use:

- $\sigma(p) = p + 1$ for primes
- If n is a perfect square, $\sigma(n) = n^2 + n + 1$
- $\sigma(2^n) = 2^{n+1} - 1$
- $\sigma(p^n)$ for primes can be found using the formula for geometric series
- $\sigma(xy) = \sigma(x) \cdot \sigma(y)$
- If n is a multiple of 7, then $\sigma(n)$ is a multiple of 8

Not all these conjectures are true. Challenge all conjectures with numeric examples. Participants may recognize in this set that the behavior for primes and nonprimes are different, or that the behavior for a number is based on its prime factorization. Both of these are important concepts that will be developed further in later problem sets with new functions.

When discussing the opener, and the followup problem (Problem 1), try to keep the focus on numeric examples—especially if you feel that *any* participant is having trouble algebraically. Some examples:

- $\sigma(13) = 1 + 13 = 14$

- $\sigma(7) = 1 + 7 = 8$

- $\sigma(91) = 112 = 14 \cdot 8$

- $\sigma(2) = 1 + 2 = 3$

- $\sigma(9) = 1 + 3 + 9 = 13$

- $\sigma(18) = 39 = 3 \cdot 13$

In Problem 2, compare two different methods participants may use here. The first is enumerating the factors of the given number, and the second is using patterns discovered in the opener or during work on Problem 1. For example, work on part (c) could go like this:

$$\sigma(5 \cdot 49) = 1 + 5 + 7 + 35 + 49 + 245 = 342$$

or like this:

$$\sigma(5 \cdot 49) = \sigma(5) \cdot \sigma(49) = 6 \cdot 57 = 342$$

Look for any participant able to synthesize these methods by expanding $\sigma(5)$ and $\sigma(49)$:

$$\sigma(5) \cdot \sigma(49) = (1+5)(1+7+49) = 1+5+7+35+49+245$$

This gets to the heart of why multiplicative functions may behave as they do. If this comes up in this problem set or in a future problem set, try to bring it to everyone's attention. Some problems in later problem sets are intended to key on this concept.

Problem 3 will be revisited, but some participants may be interested especially in part (b), since it asks to identify "perfect" numbers without saying so.

Problems beyond Problem 3 will generally be revisited in "Important Stuff" later in the course. Only discuss a problem with the whole group if you are sure the entire group has had a chance to work on it. For Problem Set 1, almost all discussion should be about Problems 1 and 2.

Problem Set 2

Goals of the Problem Set

As with Problem Set 1, this problem set introduces a new multiplicative function, here called the a function. Names of functions are consistent throughout the course, but only the four functions with Greek letter names $\phi, \sigma, \tau,$ and μ, have mathematical relevance outside this course. The goal here is to recognize consistent behavior: that the a function behaves "like" the σ function in significant ways.

A lesser goal of this problem set is to familiarize participants with sigma notation for summations (not related to the "sigma" function). This notation will be used more and more frequently as the course progresses, and this is a good opportunity to check or develop the notation before it becomes more relevant.

An optional goal is to present the number-line model for summing a series. See the details about Problem 3 below. The "comparison test" for series will be useful in later problem sets.

Notes on the Problems

Some participants may recognize that the a function given here is the same as the A function given in Problem Set 1, even though it is not described the same way: $A(n)$ was defined as $\frac{\sigma(n)}{n}$. Ask participants who recognize this to prove that the two functions must always behave the same—a proof involves writing the reciprocals using the least common denominator, which is always n. Also, don't bring this up to the whole group unless you are certain everyone has had exposure to the A function in Problem 3 of Problem Set 1.

The opener here should proceed similarly to the opener of Problem Set 1. Here are some conjectures like the ones from Problem Set 1:

- $a(p) = 1 + \frac{1}{p}$ for primes
- If n is a perfect square, $a(n) = 1 + \frac{1}{n} + \frac{1}{n^2}$
- $a(2^n) = 2 - \frac{1}{2^n}$
- $a(p^n)$ for primes can be found using the formula for geometric series
- $a(xy) = a(x) \cdot a(y)$
- If n is a multiple of 7, then $\sigma(n)$ is a multiple of $\frac{8}{7}$

As before, ask participants to verify conjectures by focusing on numeric examples, or by determining values for $a(n)$ when n isn't listed.

Problem 1 gives some cases to check against $a(xy) = a(x) \cdot a(y)$. The product for part (a), $\frac{7}{3}$, is given in the table. Parts (c) through (e) are designed to help participants recognize that $a(xy) = a(x) \cdot a(y)$ isn't always true. Some may write their suspected answer for part (e) without computing it.

Problem 2 is closely tied to Problem 1, as these are the expanded expressions for each $a(n)$ in all but part (d) of Problem 1. Some participants may use this problem as a basis for proving why $a(xy) = a(x) \cdot a(y)$ works when it does, and why it fails when it does. Specifically, the product in part (d) includes additional cross terms such as $\frac{1}{6}$ twice, and this never happens when x and y are relatively prime.

Problem 3 gives an opportunity for illustrating number line addition for working with summations like

$$1 + \frac{1}{2} + \frac{1}{4} + \frac{1}{8} + \cdots$$

Here is an illustration for both the summation of $\frac{1}{2^n}$ and $\frac{1}{3^n}$:

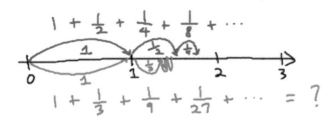

This gives participants an understanding about infinite sums, but there is a more important piece at work here, the *comparison test*:

If in two series, $a(n) \geqslant b(n)$ for each term, then $\sum a(n) \geqslant \sum b(n)$.

This concept will be useful in proving that the harmonic series $1 + \frac{1}{2} + \frac{1}{3} + \frac{1}{4} + \cdots$ diverges, since another smaller series can be found that also diverges.

Problem Set 3

Goals of the Problem Set

This problem set introduces a new multiplicative function called k. The technical definition is that $k(n)$ is the number of distinct solutions to $xy = 0$ in mod n. We present the function slightly differently here, as the number of products xy that are multiples of n when x and y range from 0 to $n - 1$. Depending on your group's familiarity with modular arithmetic, you might consider using the more technical version right away. One of the goals of this problem set is to develop a familiarity with the notation of modular arithmetic, which will be used more frequently as the course goes on.

This problem set also gives the formal definition of a multiplicative function for the first time, and asks participants to come up with some functions fitting the definition. This is a good way to wrap up this problem set (Problem 6) regardless of how far participants get through the material.

Notes on the Problems

Use the handout for Problem Set 3 (a large multiplication table) for the opener. The multiplication table is oriented so that the product at coordinates (x, y) is xy. You might consider calculating some other value of $k(n)$ as a whole group before proceeding. Composite n works best: $n = 9$ and $n = 10$ are good choices.

The opener will take a long time to complete. You might suggest to groups that they each work on a specific value of n, then compare work when finished. If doing this, be careful as errors can easily be made when counting solutions.

It is not intended for participants to use the multiplication table for all 24 values of n. Rather, they should begin coming up with conjectures similar to the ones from the previous problem sets. For example, if p is prime, $k(p) = 2p - 1$. When talking with the whole group about this problem, ask why this must be true for any prime. This fact can be concluded: if ab is a multiple of p and p is prime, then either a is a multiple of p or b is a multiple of p. This corresponds to the Zero Product Property for real numbers. Note that this property does not work for any composite number.

Problems 3 and 4 help introduce modular arithmetic. Problem 3's "units digit" arithmetic corresponds to parts (a) and (b) of Problem 4. For part (e), an input-output table may be helpful. Some participants found the second answer to part (e) by noting that 4 was an answer, and normally the other answer would be -4, but in mod 9, -4 equals 5.

Problem 5 is significant and ties into this Problem Set's Problem 13 or Problem Set 4's Problem 11. Specifically, the summation in Problem 5 is infinite, but each term is less than or equal to Problem 13's summation; therefore, the summation in Problem 13 must also be infinite. This is the Bernoulli proof that the harmonic series $1 + \frac{1}{2} + \frac{1}{3} + \frac{1}{4} + \cdots$ is infinite. Work through these two problems consecutively with the full group, once the group has had time to do both, or at the beginning of Problem Set 5 (whichever comes first). The result of Problem 13 is significant mathematically, and a similar problem is at the core of Problem Set 10. But, if possible, only have a discussion about this problem after the groups have had a try. If your group does not get to Problem 5 in this set, begin Problem Set 4 with it.

At PCMI 2009, one participant showed a lovely demonstration for Problem 7, part (c), using a similarity demonstration.

$$\frac{1}{4} + \frac{1}{16} + \frac{1}{64} + \cdots = \frac{1}{3}$$

It's short, sweet, and hard to argue against!

Problem Set 4

Goals of the Problem Set

This problem set introduces a new multiplicative function called P, the number of distinct solutions to $xy = 1$ in mod n. As with Problem Set 3, since participants may be new to modular arithmetic, the definition is not presented this way, but you may choose to use it if you feel participants are familiar enough. The P function turns out to be identical to the Euler ϕ ("fee") function which is the opening focus of Problem Set 5. For now, look for participants to recognize multiplicative behavior. Problem 4 in this set can be used to construct a proof that the P function should be multiplicative, and your group may be interested in pursuing that goal.

A second goal of the problem set is the introduction of the "child function" (Problem 5). This relationship will become a central focus as the course progresses, so consider spending time reviewing the creation of the "child function" with the whole group. One way to do this is to construct, together, the child of a different function, say $f(x) = x^2$. Then if g is the child of f, for example,

$$g(10) = f(1) + f(2) + f(5) + f(10),$$

and the value of $g(10) = 130$ can be found by direct calculation. It is good to get participants in the rhythm of this calculation early, since it will be used more and more frequently as the course advances. An immediate payoff comes in Problem Set 5 as the child of the P function is calculated, and it turns out this child is the identity function $r(n) = n$.

Notes on the Problems

In the opener, watch for any participant who notices the solutions only seem to appear in rows and columns that don't share a common factor with n. For the example $n = 10$ pictured in this problem set, these occur at $1, 3, 7, 9$ only. If this happens, you might ask the group to prove that no other column could have a number 1 more than a multiple of 10 (or pick another n: 12, 14, and 15 are good choices). This will get participants thinking about the importance of common factors. Much more difficult is the proof that in these rows and columns that *don't* have a common factor with n, a number 1 more than a multiple *must* occur. This will be addressed in a later problem set and should probably not be approached until participants are more familiar with modular arithmetic.

Problems 2 through 4 should be fairly straightforward, but note the similarities and differences between this set's Problem 4 and last set's Problem 2.

Watch for participants using mathematical techniques that are true in "regular math" in modular arithmetic. In particular, the multiple solutions in part (c), (f), and (g) are often found by participants who are less algebraically fluent. Parts (f) through (h) offer an opportunity to explore factoring, by writing the expressions as $x^3 - 1 = 0$, $x^3 + 1 = 0$, and $x^6 - 1 = 0$. Of interest to an advanced group is the factoring $x^6 - 1 = (x^3 - 1)(x^3 + 1)$ which can justify why part (h) includes every solution found in parts (f) and (g). If time permits, you might try working through these problems in other mods, especially composite mods like 15, where some of the expected rules take a twist. Problem 4 of the next set follows up on this concept.

Problems 8 and 11 are important for later work. Depending on the level of participants, they may be familiar already with the proof and result from Problem 8. As mentioned, Problem 11 depends on last set's Problem 5; if you do not get a chance to address this problem in this set, consider doing so at the start of Problem Set 5. Here is a visual proof using the "number line" style presented earlier:

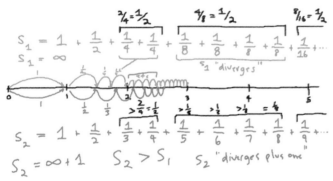

The statement "S_2 equals infinity plus one" came from a participant, and isn't mathematically accurate, but it gets the point across: each term of S_2 is greater than or equal to each term of S_1, so $S_2 \geqslant S_1$ as a sum. But we know S_1 diverges (has no maximum), so S_2, which is greater, must also diverge.

Problem Set 5

Goals of the Problem Set

The primary goal of this problem set is the boxed problem between Problems 2 and 3. It asks participants to combine the calculation of the ϕ function, introduced in this problem set, with the "child function" construction introduced in Problem Set 4. If participants have not yet learned how to determine the "child function", let them carefully work on Problem 2, or pick your own function, such as $f(x) = x^2$ or $f(x) = x^3$, to work through the child calculation. The payoff that $r(x) = x$ is only satisfying if both these concepts are well-learned, so allow participants plenty of time to work on Problems 1 and 2 of this set before the boxed problem.

This problem set also wraps up a fair amount of the material that's come before it, so you might consider including a "wrap up" at the end of the problem set including things that participants have learned, and remaining open questions.

Notes on the Problems

Problem 1 introduces the ϕ ("fee") function using its usual mathematical definition. Participants should quickly notice that ϕ is identical to P from Problem Set 4, and some may wish to pursue a proof immediately. Such a proof is difficult to come by (see Problem Set 4's comments) but Problem 13 leads in that direction. If it is true that $ab = k$ and $ac = k$ in mod n with $b \neq c$, then $a(b - c) = 0$ in mod n, and particularly $(b - c)$ can't be a multiple of n. If participants ask about this right away, encourage them to wait for the later problems, since they may miss out on the Important Stuff if they spend too much time here. Some participants may find general rules for $\phi(n)$ for specific types of n, such as $\phi(p^n) = p^n - p^{n-1}$.

Problem 2 revisits the child definition given in Problem Set 4, while $g(n)$ should be a familiar function: it is the same as the a function from Problem Set 2. (This question is not asked directly, but many will notice, and a discussion about Problem 2 is likely to bring this out.)

Note also that in Problems 1 and 2, participants are asked to make identical calculations: $g(3)$, $g(5)$, $g(15)$, then $g(2)$, $g(7)$, $g(14)$. This again attacks the concept of the multiplicative function. You may also want to address the fact that for both ϕ and g, the multiplicative property does not hold when x and y share a common factor – for example, $\phi(20) \neq \phi(2)\phi(10)$, but it does equal $\phi(4)\phi(5)$.

Problem 4 may help prepare participants for some of what is to come in future problem sets. In prime moduli, things generally behave "normally" – in this case, quadratic equations won't have more than 2 solutions (some will still have only 0 or 1). But in composite moduli, such as the ones picked here, there may be more than 2 solutions. As participants may discover as they work through these kinds of problems, the solutions in composite moduli can be found by using the primes. For example, the solutions in mod 15 can be found by matching up each solution in mod 3 (0 and 1) with each solution in mod 5 (also 0 and 1). The two extra solutions are the number that is 0 mod 3 and 1 mod 5 (6), and the number that is 1 mod 3 and 0 mod 5 (10). In mod 105 this leads to the eight possible solutions. If no one discovers this, there will be plenty of other chances, and there is no need to force this concept here. For those who do use this, encourage them to try Problem 18, where the same logic can be applied.

Problem Set 6

Goals of the Problem Set

One goal of this problem set is to begin to describe multiplicative functions' behavior more systematically. In particular, participants should learn that they can give a "formula" for a multiplicative function in terms of its prime factorization. Most of the problems in this set involve functions where the formula does not depend on the values of the primes, just the number of primes and their exponents. Later problems (Problem 8) and future sets will ask similar questions where the value of the primes also matter in the formula.

Some participants may not feel these formulas fully describe functions, but they do; formal mathematical notation typically involves a product symbol, such as

$$\phi(n) = n \prod_{p|n} \left(1 - \frac{1}{p}\right)$$

The capital π is a product symbol, instead of a summation symbol, and p|n is read as "p divides n", identifying the prime divisors of n. The notation isn't necessary (and isn't seen until Problem Set 14), but participants may want to write such descriptions in sentences as early as this problem set in formally defining functions like t and u.

A related goal is the recognition that (at least for these functions) if a parent is multiplicative, so is its child. Steps leading to a proof of this fact are presented throughout the problem sets, and advanced participants may reach this point. All participants will recognize it as seemingly true over the next few opening problems.

Notes on the Problems

The opener may take some time, but watch for participants recognizing common behavior between outputs. For example, a participant may realize that u(6), u(10), and u(15) must all be equal, because the values they are built from (in the outputs of t) are all identical. Group discussion could center around this, and how those observations build the table for Problem 2.

Also for Problem 2, watch for participants observing the "Pascal's triangle" relationships in the table. Ask participants in their groups to explain why the pattern exists, and whether or not it continues in both the vertical and horizontal directions.

Problems 5 and 6 may be skipped if time is short. Problems 4 and 7 are more central to course progress. For Problem 7, consider working through the numeric example $n = 21$, especially to show that $\phi(21) = (3 - 1)(7 - 1) = 12$. This graphic may be helpful:

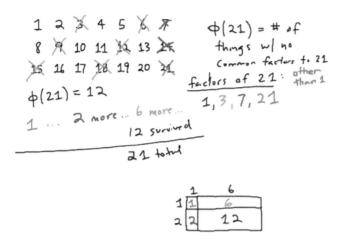

In the bottom right is an expansion box of $(1+2)(1+6)$ to show all the terms that come up in part (c) of Problem 7 when $n = 21$. If time permits, try this with a larger prime, like $n = 33$ or $n = 35$, products exactly two odd primes.

Problem Set 7

Goals of the Problem Set

The main goal of this problem set is a deeper understanding of how to solve equations in composite moduli. This problem set uses mod 60, while a similar problem in the next problem set uses mod 63. The concept is that if a and b are relatively prime with $ab = n$, then you can use mod a and mod b to solve equations in mod n. Specifically, any solution in mod a can be paired with any solution in mod b to form a distinct solution in mod n.

This is of practical importance in equation solving: solving $x^2 = 2x$ directly in mod 60 is tedious and difficult, but solving it in mod 5 and mod 12 are much simpler. Then, these solutions generate all the solutions in mod 60. Note that the table here is deliberately laid out as a 5-by-12 grid to make these connections (especially the solutions in mod 12) more clear.

This is of mathematical importance as well. As it states in the opener, if $f(n)$ is the number of solutions to an equation in mod n, in this case $f(60) = f(5) \cdot f(12)$. It turns out this is true whenever a and b are relatively prime, so *for any equation*, the number of solutions mod n is a multiplicative function! (See the openers for Problem Sets 3 and 4.)

Specifically, this means the ϕ function is multiplicative, since it is identical to the number of solutions to $xy = 1$ mod n. This generates a vast stream of multiplicative functions.

If participants arrive at any of these concepts in this problem set, terrific! But there is plenty of time for these ideas to develop.

Notes on the Problems

We found the speed of participants was highly variable in the problems of this set, which is why Problems 4-6 are repeated on Problem Set 8's problem set.

As participants work through the opener, make sure they do not miss any solutions in the smaller mods, particularly mod 12. Some may assume that there cannot be more than two solutions, which is not correct – point them to problems in previous sets where this was the case.

The table in Problem 2 is slightly different from the table in the opener, since 60 is used instead of 0. You might point out that in mod 60, 0 and 60 are the same number, so the tables are really identical up to a shift. This will come out in Problem 3 for certain, as some participants will whip through it while others will want to construct a new table like the ones before.

Problem 4 may be skipped (it's repeated as Problem 3 in the next set) if time is tight. Have participants *use the overlaid grid* to determine the diameters and centers of the circles. There are multiple ways to work through this problem geometrically, especially to find the center and diameter of the centered circle. This is likely to be too difficult for many, and we suggest asking participants to just use the grid and its scale ($1/36 = 1$ box). Those who want more of a challenge should try Problem 16, which asks to continue finding the center and diameter of more small circles, ideally using methods from coordinate geometry or other means.

Problems 5 and 6 may be skipped (repeated as Problem 5 in the next set) but should be pursued if possible. If groups do not have access to CAS technology, consider using TI-Nspire CAS TE, software for PC or Mac, or other programs (Mathematica, Maple, others). Also of interest is Wolfram Alpha, a website where CAS calculations can be executed in a similar manner to a Web search. Problems 5 and 6 preview the increasing use of formal expressions and power series that will appear in later problem sets, and Problem 6 is a surprising use of polynomial algebra to show the distribution of four dice rolls, which most participants are unlikely to have seen before. The histogram of this distribution looks surprisingly close to a normal or binomial distribution, and when more dice are thrown, the results are even closer.

Problem Set 8

Goals of the Problem Set

As with Problem Set 7, one main goal is an understanding of how to solve an equation in a composite mod. The grid used here is 7-by-9. There is practical value in the method, since solving in mod 63 directly is difficult – and quickly gets more difficult with larger mods, while a large composite mod can be broken into two or more small mods. And if there is no solution in any of the small mods, there is no solution in the large one.

Two other goals present themselves in Problems 3-7. The circles problem, first seen in Problem Set 7, should be addressed here, and Problem 4 offers an interesting algebraic method for finding the diameters of the circles. This track comes to a head in Problem Set 10, where the circles are used to prove that the summation

$$1 + \frac{1}{4} + \frac{1}{9} + \frac{1}{16} + \cdots < 2$$

In particular, the sum must be finite, unlike the harmonic sum presented earlier.

Problems 5-7 pick up on the thread of algebraic expansion, which will primarily be used to answer the "sum of two squares" and "sum of four squares" problems that are an increased focus in later problem sets.

The ground work for the rest of the course is in this problem set, so care should be taken to see that the three concepts presented here are well understood. If not, or if time is short, allocate some time in a future problem set to catch up.

Notes on the Problems

Problems 1 and 2 point out a piece about multiplicative functions that some participants may have forgotten here: the method only works when the two given numbers are relatively prime. For 63, you might bring up the fact that $63 = 3 \cdot 21$ also, but solving the equation in mod 3 and in mod 21 would not have been helpful – knowing solutions in mod 3 gives no additional information if you already know the solutions in mod 21! It is the reason why Problem Set 7's opener uses mod 5 and mod 12 instead of a different product (specifically, 6 and 10 as applied to Problem 2).

Problem 4 should be fairly straightforward, but watch for participants making several potential errors including using the diameter instead of its reciprocal, using radii instead of diameters, or (most common) using the wrong circle's diameter. Only circles that are mutually tangent should be used, so the next small circle uses $a = 1$ and $b = 9$. Later problem sets (see Problem Set 9, Problem 10 among others) will explore the circles that fall in between. The result here is a variant of Descartes' original result for *four* circles that are mutually tangent:

$$2(a^2 + b^2 + c^2 + d^2) = (a + b + c + d)^2$$

Here, an externally tangent circle uses a negative value for the variable. The special case, when $d = 0$, occurs when one of the circles has an infinite diameter... and in this case, it would look like a line.

Some participants may have trouble reading the result of Problem 7's expansion. It is easier if it's written without exponents! Instead of pr^3s write $prrrs$... This can help a lot, and explains why the results of the expansion do not account for the order of terms.

Depending on the group's speed, a discussion of Problem 8 may be of interest. The method of Problem 8 is sometimes known as the Chinese Remainder Theorem and can be used to quickly calculate all the solutions for mod n if $n = ab$ where a and b are relatively prime. Consider demonstrating a different equation or modulus if doing a whole-group discussion – one option is to use the opener from Problem Set 7.

Problem Set 9

Goals of the Problem Set

There are two main goals of this problem set: setting up Problem Set 10's proof about the sum of reciprocal squares, and introducing the sums-of-squares problems that will become the biggest focus beyond Problem Set 10. Make sure participants work through Problems 3-8, and that they are discussed before Problem Set 10 begins.

Unusually, it means the opener (and Problems 1-2 that follow) may be skipped if time is expected to be tight. The opener is interesting, and shows a "torus" approach to modular arithmetic that can be a powerful concept, but is not as central to the rest of the course.

Notes on the Problems

For the opener, consider placing the next few numbers as a whole group: 11 goes in coordinate $(1,4)$, 12 in $(2,5)$, up to 14 and maybe 15. One interesting thing to observe later is that each cell in the diagram is $21x + 50y$ in mod 70 (or, alternately, $21x - 20y$). Linearity still applies, so (for example) the value at coordinate $(3,2)$ must be 21 more than the value at coordinate $(2,2)$. If participants notice and use this linearity, bring it up in whole-group discussion.

At PCMI 2009 participants were given toruses (made from halves of "pool noodles") marked with the 10-by-7 grid, markers, and instructions to pick any spot for 0 and move up and to the right "forever". Doing so created the table given in the opener. You might also tell participants to think of the paper as connected from top-to-bottom and left-to-right.

Make completely sure everyone gets the right answers for Problems 3-5. In Problem Set 10 two "curved paths" will be shown, both finite in length, that must be longer than the sum of the diameters of the given circles. For Problem 3, emphasize in discussion that it is unknown whether the drawn path is finite or infinite in length.

Also, bring up this connection between Problems 3 and 5: the terms of Problem 5's $b(n)$ are always terms in the summation they found in Problem 3. One of the questions in Problem Set 10's opener asks about this connection. 2520 is the smallest number for which $b(n)$ includes the first 10 terms of the summation, since it is the smallest number evenly divisible by all of 1 through 10.

Problems 6-8 show a surprising application to counting the number of ways to write a number as the sum of two squares, one that connects to the polynomial power expansions in Problem Set 8. Encourage participants to square the polynomial by hand, since some may come up with interesting ways to do it. An "expansion box" method is useful here and has a nice parallel to the grid that participants will receive for Problem Set 11's opener. Note that Problem 8 is necessary here: Problem 7 doesn't make much sense without 8, so if for some reason participants don't get through Problem 8, work on 6-8 sometime prior to Problem Set 11.

Problem Set 10

Goals of the Problem Set

There are two goals of this problem set. The first is a proof that the summation

$$1 + \frac{1}{4} + \frac{1}{9} + \frac{1}{16} + \cdots$$

is finite, and, as a consequence, there is a maximum value to the b function presented here (and in previous problem sets' Neat Stuff). Jakob Bernoulli first proved this sum had an upper bound of 2, which is the bound that participants should find here. The exact value of the sum was found by Euler, decades later, and is the rather remarkable $\frac{\pi^2}{6}$. (Do not share this value with participants unless they bring it up, or until Problem Set 13.)

The second is to cement two findings about the ϕ function: that $\phi(n)$ is also the number of solutions to $xy = 1$ in mod n, and that the sum of the ϕ function over the divisors of n equals n. This last result was found in Problem Set 5, using the "child" function, but the treatment here offers more perspective on how the statement might be proved. Its placement here also reminds participants about the "child" relationship, which will be revisited thoroughly in Problem Sets 11–14.

Notes on the Problems

In the opener, watch for participants unsure how to use the path. Some may not have noticed that within each circle, the total distance traveled by the path equals the diameter of that circle. Others may not recall the exact diameters. Once they are led through which circles make up $b(4)$, the rest of the problem should be quick.

There are multiple ways to approach the dashed path. One is to determine the length and width of each piece; an interesting relationship involving Pythagorean triples emerges (Problem 9 asks about this). There is an easier way, which is to take the vertical and horizontal path segments and move them to the axes. This makes the length of the dotted path much more obvious, as the sum of the (infinite!) horizontal segments is 1 and the sum of the vertical segments is 1/2. If no one thinks of moving or combining paths in this way, this is worth showing to the whole group.

At PCMI 2009, a participant found an unexpected lower bound for the length of the dotted path by drawing a path directly from $(1, 1/2)$ to $(0, 0)$ (and staying on the path in the upper right for the large circle). The length of this path turns out to be the golden ratio! While other, better upper bounds exist, this was really surprising, so you might ask for lower bounds as an additional problem.

Problems 5 through 7 follow up on some concepts about the ϕ function. In particular, Problems 5 and 6 suggest a proof that the ϕ and P functions are identical, and Problem 7 gives a method for constructing the set $\{1, 2, \ldots, n\}$ starting with ϕ sets that come from the divisors of n. Problem 7 can be generalized to a proof that the "child" function of ϕ must be the identity $f(n) = n$.

Problem 8 is extremely interesting and connects the two concepts of this problem set. If time permits, have participants work on this one! The results are really quite amazing.

Problem Set 11

Goals of the Problem Set

This problem set introduces the process of constructing the *parent* of a function. The particular interest here is $\mu(n)$, called the Möbius function. The end purpose of this is that the functions for the number of ways to write a number as the sum of two or four squares is messy and sporadic – for example, the sum of two squares function $s_2(n)$ has many zero values, often consecutively, but then a 4 or 8 or 12, and there is no maximum value for s_2. It turns out that the *parent* of s_2 is incredibly simple and leads to an easily-understood, computable definition for s_2: for $n > 1$, $s_2(n)$ is 4 times the difference between the number of 1 mod 4 factors of n and the number of 3 mod 4 factors of n. This remarkable formula, and another one for $s_4(n)$, are the capstones for the course, but require ground work on constructing parent functions.

Additionally, the Mobius function μ is the last of the four traditional multiplicative functions seen in a number theory course, and at the core of Mobius inversion, is a technique that can be used to directly build the parent from any child function. If a is the parent of b, then

$$a(n) = \sum_{d|n} b(d)\mu\frac{n}{d}$$

Some of the Neat and Tough Stuff problems touch on this connection, but it is not part of the main goal of this problem set or the course.

Notes on the Problems

Participants should have completed the table for m, t (now called by its usual mathematical name τ), and u. Calculating the parent function, in general, is challenging at first; one workable method is to place a grid on a transparency that illustrates what outputs "feed" others in the parent-child relationship. For example, $\tau(10) = m(1) + m(2) + m(5) + m(10)$ and on a transparency this can be slid up or down to establish, for example, $m(10) = z(1) + z(2) + z(5) + z(10)$.

Some may be surprised to see that $\mu(n)$ can be negative, especially since none of the other functions in the table have negative outputs. If this comes up, have a quick discussion about how it is built. The sidenote to this opener may also help. Some participants will want to immediately try to write a rule for $\mu(n)$ (see Problem 9), and this may be surprisingly difficult. If someone asks you may want to introduce them to the term "square free", which can help to define μ more succinctly. A capper might be to ask for $\mu(n)$ for some large factorable n, such as 510510, which is the product

$$510510 = 2 \cdot 3 \cdot 5 \cdot 7 \cdot 11 \cdot 13 \cdot 17$$

Problem 2 is the first of many where multiplying through by the expression

$$\frac{1}{1^s} + \frac{1}{2^s} + \frac{1}{3^s} + \frac{1}{4^s} + \cdots$$

will produce a child function. Specifically, if b is the child of a, then

$$\left(\frac{a(1)}{1^s} + \frac{a(2)}{2^s} + \frac{a(3)}{3^s} + \cdots \right) \left(\frac{1}{1^s} + \frac{1}{2^s} + \frac{1}{3^s} + \cdots \right) =$$

$$\frac{b(1)}{1^s} + \frac{b(2)}{2^s} + \frac{b(3)}{3^s} + \cdots$$

Over the next few problem sets, this will become increasingly prominent, so keep an ear out for anyone recognizing this connection to the topic (and direct them to Problems 13-15 of this set).

Ask participants to use the table for Problem 4, even if they have completed the table for this function previously in some other way. Problems 4 and 6 are meant as a reminder of this previous material and should be covered even if you think everyone already knows it, and the rhythm of these problems should give some ideas about how the table for Problem 7 might be computed directly. Problem 4's table can be used nicely to estimate the average value of the s_2 function, which will be Problem Set 14's opener.

Problem Set 12

Goals of the Problem Set

This problem set establishes some connections between infinite sums and infinite products. Many number theory results depend on this "sum-to-product" concept, especially when showing that a particular sum or product must be finite or infinite. The products A and B are "edge cases", an infinite number of things being multiplied together, but most of them are close to 1. By rewriting these products as sums, you can get a better picture of whether the product converges or diverges. See Problem Set 12, Problems 9 and 10 for more complex examples tied to this set's Problems 2 and 3.

Likewise, an infinite sum may be easier to work with when written as a infinite product, and this is a particularly useful thing to do when the terms in the sum are the successive outputs of a multiplicative function. One purpose of the remaining problem sets is to give participants some flavor of this style of work.

A second purpose is to find a rule for the sum-of-two-squares function, based on its parent. This rule was originally found by Fermat, and while a proof is outside the scope of this course, the rule is immediate from the parent-child relationship. One secondary result, also interesting, is that the number of 1 mod 4 factors of any positive number must be at least the number of 3 mod 4 factors; otherwise, S_2 would be negative.

Notes on the Problems

Overall, while a CAS may be helpful for some of the algebra, we intend it to be done by hand. Doing the algebra by hand encourages participants to look for patterns, and they may realize more quickly why this multiplication replicates the parent-child relationship between functions. Encourage participants not to use technology on these problems unless it is necessary.

The opener should be relatively quick and is intended for participants to practice their work on parent calculation before Problem 4. Many participants will react with an "I already know this" when they realize the "ego" function is actually good old ϕ. And that's fine. One way to wrap up discussion on this is to point out the four major number theory functions: ϕ, τ, σ, μ. Participants have now found that ϕ is the grandparent of σ, and μ is the great-grandparent of τ, with some surprisingly simple functions in between.

Problems 2 and 3 may prove difficult for some participants, but they should get through it working through the parts as listed (the parts are intended to be roughly parallel in structure between Problems 2 and 3). In Problem 2, the goal is for participants to recognize that *any* term in the form $\frac{1}{n}$ is attainable, *in exactly one way*, and this is why the product is equal to the sum of the harmonic series. Some participants may be eager to try to evaluate the geometric series listed, but this is something to table until later. At PCMI 2009, one participant conjectured that any product in the form of Problem 2, a product of an infinite number of things greater than 1, would have to be infinite – which turns out not to be true for Problem 3. If anyone makes this conjecture, show it to everyone, then let them decide (perhaps not even during this problem set) whether or not it is true.

We hope participants will find the R_2 function amazing and simple. A full-group discussion on Problem 7 can be a good closer for this problem set, and you might consider asking participants to directly calculate the number of ways to write large numbers as the sum of two squares (see Problem 10; another good choice is $5 \cdot 13 \cdot 29 = 1885$).

Problem 8 can lead interested participants to a proof that if a function is multiplicative, its child must also be multiplicative (Problem 18).

Problem Set 13

Goals of the Problem Set

The largest goal of this problem set is for participants to determine a formula for the number of ways to write n as the sum of four squares. Some participants may already know the "four squares theorem", that any positive n *can* be written as the sum of four squares, but are very unlikely to have seen this before. And the formula is amazingly simple:

$s_4(n) = 8$ times the sum of divisors of n, except those divisors that are multiples of 4.

As a wrap-up to the problem set, consider asking participants to determine $s_4(120)$, then verify by looking deep into the expansion of the polynomial in Problem 1.

A secondary goal is a deeper look at the calculations involving products of infinite sums, particularly multiplying through by

$$\frac{1}{1^s} + \frac{1}{2^s} + \frac{1}{3^s} + \cdots$$

and searching for a similar expression that "undoes" this. In doing so, parents and children can now be calculated algebraically and directly. Overall, the key concept is using algebraic expressions as placeholders for calculations, and this concept has applications throughout the high school and collegiate math curriculum.

As mentioned previously, this is a good time to tell students the exact value:

$$1 + \frac{1}{4} + \frac{1}{9} + \frac{1}{16} + \cdots = \frac{\pi^2}{6}$$

Many proofs are available online. Here is the simplest proof we found; you might consider going through this proof with participants who are familiar with the concepts involved. Note that this is not a complete, formal proof, but gives the outline of its contents. If a proof is not given, try using a CAS or other computer program, some of which give the exact value of the summation.

Proof. If x is any angle in radians, the power series definition states that

$$\sin x = x - \frac{x^3}{6} + \frac{x^5}{120} - \cdots$$

Now consider the graph of $y = \sin x$ as if it were a polynomial. It crosses the axis for any multiple of π, therefore

$$\sin x = Ax(\pi - x)(\pi + x)(2\pi - x)(2\pi + x)(3\pi - x) \cdots$$

where A is some multiplier. Now use difference of squares factoring:

$$\sin x = Ax(\pi^2 - x^2)(4\pi^2 - x^2)(9\pi^2 - x^2)\cdots$$

The coefficient of x must be 1 (since $\sin x = x - \frac{x^3}{6} + \cdots$). The multiplier A can be removed by dividing through all terms by their constant:

$$\sin x = x\left(1 - \frac{x^2}{\pi^2}\right)\left(1 - \frac{x^2}{4\pi^2}\right)\left(1 - \frac{x^2}{9\pi^2}\right)\cdots$$

Now consider the expansion of the right side. The expansion gives

$$\sin x = x - \left(\frac{x^3}{\pi^2} + \frac{x^3}{4\pi^2} + \frac{x^3}{9\pi^2} + \cdots\right) + \cdots$$

What is the coefficient of the x^3 term? The power series definition says it is $-\frac{1}{6}$. But this means that

$$-\frac{x^3}{6} = -\frac{x^3}{\pi^2}\left(1 + \frac{1}{4} + \frac{1}{9} + \frac{1}{16} + \cdots\right)$$

Therefore

$$\frac{\pi^2}{6} = 1 + \frac{1}{4} + \frac{1}{9} + \frac{1}{16}$$

which is the desired result. ∎

Especially advanced participants may wish to continue to find the coefficient of x^5 in a similar manner, which can be used (along with some other creative work) to find the sum of reciprocal fourth powers (Problem Set 15, Problem 10).

Notes on the Problems

In Problem 1, many participants will miss $2^2 + 0^2 + 0^2 + 0^2$, which generates an additional 8 solutions (giving the total of 24).

Problem 2 may take a long time for some participants, especially those who have not investigated the effect of multiplying by this expression. Problem 3 directs them toward that investigation. Some participants will not advance past Problem 3 in this set, and that's fine.

Problem 4 follows up on the introduction of μ from Problem Set 12, and can be skipped. But be sure participants will be able to recognize it – it's the function that emerges in Problem 5 and in Problem 8.

Problem Set 14

Goals of the Problem Set

The goal of this problem set is some final work on sum-to-product conversion, especially Problems 4-6. Problem 6 is a strong culmination for this segment of the course, especially if students now know the $\frac{\pi^2}{6}$ summation.

A second goal is to produce an observation about the s_2 function and its average value. Even though s_2 varies wildly, its average value becomes more and more consistent. This is a good tactic for other wildly-varying functions or statistical data: consider looking at the average of terms, whether a moving average or (in this case) the running average as n goes from 1 to higher and higher values.

Notes on the Problems

The graph from Problem Set 11 can be extremely helpful in explaining why the average value of $s_2(n)$ approaches π. Draw the circle $x^2 + y^2 = 49$ on the page: its area is 49π, so there should be approximately 49π lattice points inside the circle. (It won't be exact, but close.) As n grows, the number of lattice points inside $x^2 + y^2 = n$ will remain close to $n\pi$, and in particular the ratio (given in Problem 7) comes closer and closer to π as n grows. Participants may come up with pictures like this one to illustrate what is happening:

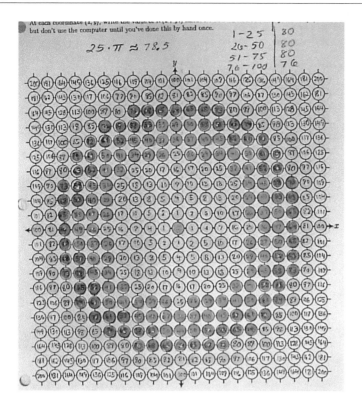

At each coordinate (x, y), write the value of ... ...
but don't use the computer until you've done this by hand once.

$25 \cdot \pi \approx 78.5$

1-25	80
26-50	80
51-75	80
76-100	76

Problems 2 and 3 may be difficult for some participants; Problem 2 is difficult for those who do not recall the formula for the sum of a geometric series, and those who can't figure this out should just look on with others. Problem 3 may be difficult conceptually; ask what would happen if there were a finite number of primes, both to the right side and to the left side of the equation.

Problems 4-6 are connected, though they do not appear so at first; have participants try to make the connections themselves. The result is a very interesting one, an infinite product of terms less than 1 where the product isn't 0. If time permits, work on Problem 8 to show the connection between it and Problem 6. The probability that two positive integers drawn at random do not share any common factors is exactly $\frac{6}{\pi^2}$.

Problem Set 15

Goals of the Problem Set

The goal of this problem set is to review the ideas of the entire course. This problem set is optional. You may prefer to have participants write their own review problems for this set.

Notes on the Problems

All problems are review problems, divided in categories by roughly when that concept was most central to the course.

CHAPTER

3

Teaching Notes

This section consists of two parts: 1) the design principles for the courses in the *Mathematics for Teaching* series, and strategies developed through the PCMI experiences for teaching the materials in ways that help participants figure out the mathematics for themselves and 2) general comments on teaching   and suggestions related to specific problem sets.

Series

Design Principles

The premises underlying the development of the *Mathematics for Teaching* courses include:

- A basic principle is "exposure before closure," where the learner uses examples to build intuition.

- The problems have multiple points of entry where everyone, regardless of the level of confidence or experience, can begin.

- The problems explicitly link different content areas and encourage learners to seek multiple representations and solutions.

- A problem presented from one perspective (algebra, say) may be repeated in another (geometrically, for example).

- Problems often foreshadow key ideas that are not introduced formally until later problem sets.

- The problems repeat and connect throughout all of the sets. The goal is to have the learners begin to look for connections rather than being surprised when they notice relationships.

"Habits of mind" for participants

1. Based on the work at PCMI and in other implementation sites, the following suggestions for participants in how they should approach the mathematics have been instrumental in enabling them to be successful in the course:

    - Being systematic in keeping track of work, including noting observations and questions along with numeric solutions.
    - Working in pairs and groups emphasizing communication to promote clear articulation of ideas about the mathematics.
    - Being open to multiple strategies, methods, and interpretations, and appreciation of the value of tolerating, discussing, comparing, reconciling, connecting different methods and answers.
    - Learning to listen to each other—expecting and probing for a high standard of support and justification for conclusions.
    - Clearly understanding questions and directions.
    - Asking good questions that will prompt others to start thinking in new ways.
    - Recognizing the value of hands on and manipulatives, rather than going immediately to computers or calculators.

2. What to look out for:

    - Sloppy or incomplete record-keeping or insufficient descriptions of strategies for collecting data may frustrate participants. Try to guide them to establish an organized way of recording their results, observations and conjectures. This will become increasingly important for participants as the problem sets progress and the need to connect work from various problem sets increases.
    - Participants may be so engaged with a particular problem on a problem set that they do not get to all the "Important Stuff." Be careful about pacing the work to help ensure that everyone at least begins all of the problems in "Important Stuff."

- Some participants may jump to using mathematics that may be foreign to others in their group and may actually distract their peers if they begin instructing others about the mathematics.
- Focusing on obtaining numerical solutions to problems can inhibit considering deeper implications of the solutions, especially as more and more patterns emerge over the course of the problem sets; for example, carrying out the computation in $\frac{1}{2^4}$ and writing the result as $\frac{1}{16}$.
- Some participants may be relying on prior knowledge rather than arriving at answers through their own discovery, and they may be tempted to share that with others, whether it is welcome or not.
- Some participants may be using technology not only to do complicated processes but in situations where the technology masks the patterns within the work they are doing.
- As the course progresses, some participants may be getting lost in all the new material that has been covered and may need encouragement to pause and take note of what they have learned to date.

It is critical that everyone is allowed to build their understanding; prior knowledge may, in fact, get in the way of understanding.

Suggestions Specific to This Course

Some general suggestions about teaching the problem sets for this course include:

1. Because organized lists can help participants make progress and enable them to discuss their results with one another, it is useful to have them share strategies for organizing the work, paying particular attention to a strategy that is particularly informative in terms of the structure. For example, in Problem Set 1, writing the factors in pairs, then doubling the original number can provide a process for keeping track of which additional factors were created.

n	3	6	12	24	48
Factor pairs	1 3	1 6 2 3	1 12 2 6 3 4	1 24 2 12 3 8 4 6	1 48 2 24 3 16 4 12 6 8

Note that the factors wrap around and that two additional factors are added each time. One of those factors is n, and the other is $\frac{n}{3}$ a power of 2. The two additional factors occur in the same place in the list of factor pairs each time. Encouraging participants to share strategies such as these will not only help those who are struggle with organization but may also reveal different perspectives on the mathematics itself.

2. Try to keep the notation and language informal, particularly at first. For example, in Problem Set 1, for the sequence

$$18 = 2 \cdot 3 \cdot 3 = 2 \cdot 3^2$$
$$\sigma(2) = 1 + 2 = 3$$
$$\sigma(3^2) = 1 + 3 + 9 = 13$$
$$\sigma(18) = 39 = s(2) \cdot s(3^2),$$

some may want to use the notation $\sigma(3^2) = 3^0 + 3^1 + 3^2 = 13$. Encourage them to wait until the usefulness of that notation emerges from the work itself.

3. Throughout the problem sets, encourage participants to practice "delayed computation," maintaining the values to be used in a calculation without actually performing the calculation as a strategy to make patterns and connections more visible: for example, retaining denominators as powers of the same base rather than simplifying them.

4. Encourage the use of "trial and error" as a way to begin thinking about a problem. For example, using a trial and error approach in problem 1 of Problem Set 7 can lead to interesting conjectures about the location in the table of the solutions for mod 7 and mod 70.

5. CAS can be helpful in some of the problems where the algebraic expansion could get in the way of the reasoning and sense making, such as in problem Set 7, problem 6 in expanding $(x + x^2 + x^3 + x^4 + x^5 + x^6)^4$.

But participants should be encouraged to do many of the expansions by hand so they pay attention to the patterns that are evolving, which they may miss if they use technology. They should also be alert to the fact that CAS does not always work given the nature of some of the problems, for example trying to expand the polynomial that does not have a finite set of terms in Problem Set 11, Problem 2.

6. A reminder that the problem sets are designed to have multiple access points and do not require advanced prior knowledge. While some of the problems deal with topics from calculus such as convergence and divergence of series and Taylor expansions, these are not made explicit and it is not necessary to do so for participants to be successful in the course.

The Mathematical Overview contains a description of the goals for each problem set and occasionally has suggestions for shaping instruction to reach those goals. Particular suggestions for individual problem sets include the following:

Problem Set 3

The concept of modular arithmetic might be new to many in the course. Try to refrain from a "mini-lecture" and let the problems themselves develop the concept. If you have questions or concerns check with the field notes related to the introduction of "mods" for suggestions on how to incorporate the topic for students who do or do not already know the topic. Try to avoid the temptation to slow down here and put more into the problems about the topic as the development continues to be embedded in the ongoing problem sets.

At the end of class, you might summarize mods in detail using a particular example, say mod 6:

5	0	5	4	3	2	1
4	0	4	2	0	2	4
3	0	3	0	3	0	3
2	0	2	4	0	2	4
1	0	1	2	3	4	5
0	0	0	0	0	0	0
×	0	1	2	3	4	5

If participants do not suggest it, call attention to the fact that the 0s in the table are solutions to the equation

$xy = 0 \bmod 6$ and ask for an explanation of why this is true. Some may recognize that this is equivalent to $k(n)$ from the problem set.

A discussion question might be why prime numbers give particular answers. Participants should noting that if n is prime, then $k(n) = 2n - 1$. At this point, you might want to consider writing this fact as: $k(p) = 2p - 1$ using p for prime.

Problem Set 5

At this point in the course, participants should recognize the format: begin with the "function of the day," playing around with it to understand its behavior and guessing patterns.

At the close of the session, you might bring the ideas from the first four days together and ask participants what they had surprising things they had learned so far and things they were wondering about.

Possible responses for what was surprising:

- Harmonic series diverges: $1 + \frac{1}{2} + \frac{1}{3} + \frac{1}{4} + \cdots$

- How to think about categories of numbers in terms of prime, relatively prime, and composites of two prime factors.

- $a(n) = \dfrac{\sigma(n)}{n}$ is unbounded.

- Many perfect squares are multiples of 24 plus one (i.e., $1 \cdot 24 + 1 = 25, 5 \cdot 24 + 1 = 121$)

Questions that remain:

- Why is the statement - a Child of $\phi(n)$ is the identity $15 = \phi(15) + \phi(5) + \phi(3) + \phi(1)$ - true?

- How can you compute $f(a \cdot b)$ from $f(a)$ and $f(b)$ when a and b are not relatively prime?

- How do primes help deal with mods?

Problem Set 7

This might be a good time to review with the whole group finding solutions in the land of mods and making sure that the difference in finding solutions in the set of real numbers is clear. For example, in solving $4x = 8 \bmod 5$, mod 12, and mod 60, traditional algebraic methods don't necessarily work. In particular, one can't simply divide both sides by 4 – because it isn't clear that 4 has a multiplicative inverse, and the zero product property doesn't necessarily work in mod land (i.e., $4 \cdot 3 = 0 \bmod 12$, but neither factor equals 0.)

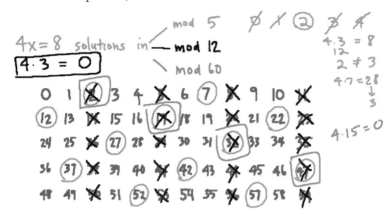

Problem Set 11

The transparencies from Friday illustrating the property that the child of the $\phi(n)$ function was the identity function can provide a visual representation of the mathematics. You can show that the four transparencies for $n = 10$ have $\phi(1)$, $\phi(2)$, $\phi(5)$, and $\phi(10)$ dots respectively and that when laid upon each other there is exactly one dot in each row and column. Since there are 10 rows there are 10 dots.

At the end of the session, you might ask participants to reflect on the properties of $\mu(n)$. Some possible conclusions:

1. $\mu(p \cdot q) = 1$ when p and q are primes.

2. $\mu(p) = -1$ when p is prime.

3. $\mu(p^n) = 0$ when $n > 1$ and p is prime.

4. $\mu(n) = 1$ when n is a product of an even number of distinct primes and if n is "square free."

5. $\mu(n) = -1$ when n is a product of an odd number of distinct primes and if n is "square free."

Problem Set 12

Problem 2 would be a good problem for discussion. Participants might notice

- each of the factors is itself an infinite geometric series whose sum can be found by using $S = \dfrac{a}{1 - r}$. The sum of the terms in the first factor is $\frac{2}{1}$, of the second factor is $\frac{3}{2}$, of the third $\frac{5}{4}$. Therefore one way of expressing the sum of the terms is $\frac{2}{1} \cdot \frac{3}{2} \cdot \frac{5}{4} \cdot \frac{7}{6} \cdots \cdots$ $\frac{p}{p-1} \cdots \cdots$. Each of the factors is greater than one, so this product must be infinitely large.

- the product is of the form

$$\left(1 + \frac{1}{1}\right)\left(1 + \frac{1}{2}\right)\left(1 + \frac{1}{4}\right)\left(1 + \frac{1}{6}\right)\cdots$$

which might relate to $\left(1 + \frac{1}{n}\right)^n$ which gets closer to e.

- There is one and only one way to get each fraction. For example

$$\frac{1}{12} = \frac{1}{2^2} \cdot \frac{1}{3} \cdot \frac{1}{1} \cdots \cdots \frac{1}{1} \cdots \cdots$$

So, the result of the expansion is the harmonic series,

$$\sum_1^{\infty} \frac{1}{n}$$

which we've shown to be divergent.

Problem Set 13

Some possible discussion questions:

1. What is a simple rule to calculate $R_4(n)$ for any n?

2. What is a simple rule to calculate $S_4(n)$ for any n?

3. How many ways are there to write 120 as a sum of squares?

Discussion Questions

- What's a simple rule to calculate
  $R_4(n)$ for any n? It's n, except it's 0 when multiples of 4
  $S_4(n)$ for any n? $S_4(10) = \sigma(10)$
      child of R_4
      S_4 sum of divisors of n $1+2+5+10=18$
          unless they're multiples of 4

$R_4(n) = n$, except if it is $0 \bmod 4$ and then it is zero. S_4 is the child of R_4. Point out that you need the background from the last two weeks to figure out the pattern for S_4. To get S_4 from R_4, multiply by the series $\left(\frac{1}{1^s} + \frac{1}{2^s} + \frac{1}{3^s} + \cdots\right)$. The numerators of the resulting series would be the S_4's. On the other hand $S_4(10) = \sigma(10)$. In simple words, $S_4(n) =$ sum of the divisors of n, except those that are multiples of 4. To find $S_4(120)$ one can write all the factors of 120 and cross those out the multiples of 4 and then add the rest together: Example: 1, 2, 3, 4, 5, 6, 8, 10, ~~12~~, 15, ~~20~~, ~~24~~, 30, ~~40~~, ~~60~~, ~~120~~. Those that remain are just the factors of 30, which have a sum of 72.

You might want to note that the actual number of ways to write 120 as the sum of four squares is $8 \cdot 72 = 576$. One possible strategy is to start by dividing 120 by 4 to get 30 and use 30 to find the factors. In this case, this method would work, however 60 does not. If you cross out the factors of 60 that are divisible by 5, the resulting set is not the factors of 15. It is, oddly, the factors of 30.

Problem Set 14

The problem in the box may take some time to finish. A typical approach is to use the table from Day 11 and add up the values for $s_2(n)$. The focus is on values as n goes from 1 to 25, so the sum the values of $s_2(n)$ for n going from 1 to 49 the average is $\frac{148}{49} = 3.020$.

While some counted circles from the handout for Day 11, others might use technology. The above approach evaluates the polynomial when $x = 1$ and thus has the effect of adding up all of the coefficients. You could also use the `polycoeffs` function on the TI-Nspire handheld to strip off the coefficients of the polynomial and put them in a list. Then add up the appropriate columns of the list to get the desired result.

For Problem 3, $\prod_p \frac{p^s}{p^s-1}$ is related to the 2009 mathematical research theme of L-functions and was essentially the same as that on the PCMI banner used in the 2009 Park City Fourth of July Parade. There, the expression was written: $\prod_p (1-p^{-s})$.

Problem Set 15

One way to bring closure might be have participants make a family tree of all of the functions studied during the course. One example is the following, where in general the parent function is on the left and the child of that function is to the right. Some functions had multiple names during the three weeks.

- $\mu(n) \to z(n) \to m(n) \to t(n)/\tau(n) \to u(n) \to v(n)$

- $p(n)/\phi(n)/ego(n) \to id(n)/r(n) \to \sigma(n)$

- The functions $a(n)$, $k(n)$, and $b(n)$ are all related to $\sigma(n)$

- $R_2(n) \to S_2(n)$ and this last function leads to $s_2(n)$

- $R_4(n) \to S_4(n)$ and this last function leads to $s_4(n)$

C H A P T E R

4

Mathematical Overview

This overview contains a sample of the mathematical themes that the development team hammered out in the process of designing the 2009 PCMI course, *Famous Functions in Number Theory* (*FFNT* from now on). It contains some of the mathematical background used when creating the problem sets as well as some mathematical extensions that never made it into the "soup" of problems that was created by PfT alumni and then went out to PCMI. It also makes explicit some of the mathematical results used in the creation of the problem sets. This part is written by people who were in on the design but were not involved in the day-to-day classes at PCMI. The areas treated in this overview include

In addition to the teachers participating in the course, PCMI hosts research programs in mathematics and education, programs for graduate students and undergraduate faculty, and institutes for staff development professionals. See `pcmi.ias.edu` for more details.

1. The use of formal algebra in number theory.

2. Summing over divisors and its connection to Dirichlet series.

3. The number of representations of an integer as the sum of two squares.

There are many more ideas that are introduced in the problem sets—concrete examples or applications of the highlighted machinery, different ways to understand some of the results, and connections to other related areas. These are described in more detail in the day-by-day facilitator notes.

One of the things that's unique about *FFNT* is how it motivates rather technical results through numerical experiments. For example, one of the main results is a beautiful theorem of Fermat:

> *Suitably counted, the number of ways a positive integer n can be written as a sum of two squares can be calculated by looking at all the positive divisors of n, ignoring the even ones, and taking the excess of the number of divisors of form $4k + 1$ over those of form $4k + 3$.*

The result is striking and surprising. What's more, the only proof we know uses some fairly advanced techniques from number theory (we sketch an outline of such a proof below). But, stepping back, how could the theorem even be conjectured? Certainly, one could look at data, but what would prompt someone to count divisors of form $4k + 1$ and $4k + 3$?

Why should the number of divisors that are 1 mod 4 be at least as large as the number that are 3 mod 4? That's a corollary to the theorem.

The instructors of *FFNT*, Bowen Kerins and Darryl Yong, devised an ingenious way to make the conjecture jump out of a numerical experiment. The approach uses several devices, developed slowly and experientially throughout the problem sets:

- Throughout the course, formal calculations with polynomials and power series are used to generate numerical data. In this case, calculations with polynomials and power series yields the values of the values of $s_2(n)$ where

$s_2(n) =$ the number of ways n can be written as a sum of two squares

The definition of s_2 is given precisely later in this overview.

- In a different thread of the *FFNT*, a notion is developed over several problem sets: a function f, defined on non-negative integers, is compiled in a certain way to produce another function g, called its "child". More precisely, $g(n)$ is the sum of the values of f over the divisors of n.

The compilation is a special case of what's known as *Dirichlet convolution*.

- This compilation process can be reversed, so that a child produces a "parent." This produces, starting with a function f, a stream of functions—ancestors and descendants of f:

$$\ldots \; f_{-3} \leftarrow f_{-2} \leftarrow f_{-1} \leftarrow f_0 = f \leftarrow f_1 \leftarrow f_2 \leftarrow f_3 \leftarrow f_4 \; \ldots$$

Here, each f_i points to its parent. This parent-child relationship is discussed in great detail in [4].

The conjecture develops, through a series of assumptions and calculations:

1. Use a generating polynomial calculation to generate data for s_2. The values of $s_2(n)$ for $n > 0$ are all divisible by 4.

2. Calculate, one value at a time, the values of the parent for $S_2(n) = \frac{s_2(n)}{4}$. These values turn out to be, conjecturally, 0 if n is even, 1 if n is 1 mod 4, and -1 if n is 3 mod 4.

3. If this is true, then $S_2(n)$ is the sum over the divisors of n of this parent function, and this is exactly the excess of the number of $4k + 1$ divisors over the

number of $4k + 3$ divisors. This is precisely the statement of Fermat's theorem on the sum of two squares.

The Kerins-Yong approach to making the statement of the theorem seem natural has all the features of a genuine mathematical investigation: experimental data is generated and analyzed, assumptions (lemmas, in fact) are stated and temporarily assumed (in order to see if they lead to interesting ideas), and precise language is used to help one frame a conjecture. The only missing piece is a proof that this all works. *FFNT* doesn't quite nail down a proof, but it provides participants with all of the necessary ingredients. After a discussion of the method leading up to the conjecture, we'll sketch out a proof here, pointing to the references for the complete details.

Children, Parents, and Dirichlet Series

This approach to conjecturing the result about sums of squares might seem natural, once one thinks of using the parent-child relationship, but this raises the question of why one would think about compiling over divisors in the first place.

One answer lies in the theory of Dirichlet series. Dirichlet introduced these series to answer combinatorial questions in number theory, and they have since found applications all over mathematics. A formal ***Dirichlet series*** is an expression of the form

$$\sum_{n=1}^{\infty} \frac{a(n)}{n^s} = a(1) + \frac{a(2)}{2^s} + \frac{a(3)}{3^s} + \cdots,$$

where a is a function defined on positive integers taking values in the complex numbers.

A function $a : \mathbb{N} \to \mathbb{C}$ is sometimes called an ***arithmetic*** function.

The word "formal" is important here—just as in other parts of *FFNT*, we think of these series as bookkeeping devices keeping track of combinatorial or numerical data. So, we don't worry about questions of convergence. This misses many of the wonderful analytic applications of such series, but it turns out that the formal algebraic properties are all we need for this discussion.

... [to] omit those parts of the subject, however, is like listening to a stereo broadcast of, say, Beethoven's Ninth Symphony, using only the left audio channel. [9], p. vii.

Dirichlet series are added and multiplied formally. Addition is done term by term:

$$\sum_{n=1}^{\infty} \frac{a(n)}{n^s} + \sum_{n=1}^{\infty} \frac{b(n)}{n^s} = \sum_{n=1}^{\infty} \frac{a(n) + b(n)}{n^s}.$$

Multiplication is also done term by term, but then one gathers up all terms with the same denominator. So, for example, if we're looking for $c(12)/12^s$ in

$$\sum_{n=1}^{\infty} \frac{a(n)}{n^s} \sum_{n=1}^{\infty} \frac{b(n)}{n^s} = \sum_{n=1}^{\infty} \frac{c(n)}{n^s}, \qquad (1)$$

then a denominator of 12^s could come only from the products

$$\frac{a(1)}{1^s} \cdot \frac{b(12)}{12^s}, \quad \frac{a(2)}{2^s} \cdot \frac{b(6)}{6^s}, \quad \frac{a(3)}{3^s} \cdot \frac{b(4)}{4^s}, \quad \frac{a(4)}{4^s} \cdot \frac{b(3)}{3^s}, \quad \frac{a(6)}{6^s} \cdot \frac{b(2)}{2^s}, \quad \frac{a(12)}{12^s} \cdot \frac{b(1)}{1^s}.$$

In general, the coefficient $c(n)$ in equation (1) is given by

$$c(n) = \sum_{d|n} a(d) \cdot b\left(\frac{n}{d}\right), \qquad (2)$$

where $\sum_{d|n}$ means that the sum is over the divisors of n.

The simplest Dirichlet series is the **Riemann zeta function**:

$$\zeta(s) = \sum_{n=1}^{\infty} \frac{1}{n^s}.$$

Eq. (2) implies a result that we'll need later:

Theorem 4.1

$$\zeta(s) \sum_{n=1}^{\infty} \frac{a(n)}{n^s} = \sum_{n=1}^{\infty} \frac{b(n)}{n^s},$$

then

$$b(n) = \sum_{d|n} a(d). \qquad (3)$$

And so we see the appearance of a sum over the divisors.

If two functions a and b, defined on non-negative integers, are related as in Equation (3), we say that b is the *child* of a (and a is the *parent* of b).

Ways to Think About It

Many functions that arise in number theory are related by this parent-child connection. For example, if e is the identity function, $e(n) = n$, then e is the parent of σ, the *sum of the divisors* function:

$$\sigma(n) = \sum_{d|n} d$$

And e is the child of the *Euler totient function* ϕ defined by

$\phi(n)$ = the number positive of integers $\leqslant n$ that are relatively prime to n

because it tuns out (See [6]) that: So, $\phi \leftarrow e \leftarrow \sigma$.

$$n = e(n) = \sum_{d \mid n} \phi(d)$$

Sums of Two Squares

A question that runs through the problem sets is:

Which integers can be written as the sum of two (integer) squares?

Participants develop some conjectures (some with proofs). For example, they conjecture that an odd prime can be written as a sum of two squares if and only if it is congruent to 1 mod 4. What about composite integers? For example, 15 can't be written as $a^2 + b^2$, but 65 can: $65 = 8^2 + 1^2$. In fact, 65 can be written as the sum of two squares in another way: $65 = 4^2 + 7^2$. This leads to a more refined question (open to experiment by high school students):

In how many ways can a positive integer be written as the sum of two squares?

For example, 5 is a sum of two squares: $5 = 2^2 + 1^2$. But we could also write 5 in other related ways:

$$
\begin{aligned}
5 &= 2^2 + 1^2 \\
&= 2^2 + (-1)^2 \\
&= (-2)^2 + (-1)^2 \\
&= (-2)^2 + 1^2 \\
&= 1^2 + 2^2 \\
&= 1^2 + (-2)^2 \\
&= (-1)^2 + (-2)^2 \\
&= (-1)^2 + 2^2.
\end{aligned}
$$

The course starts out with this counting method and calls the function that returns this count s_2. So, for example,

$s_2(5) = 8, s_2(8) = 4, s_2(14) = 0, s(9) = 4$, and $s_2(25) = 12$

Ways to Think About It

If you tabulate s_2, you see that all the values all positive integers are divisible by 4. Essentially, $s_2(n)$ is the number of lattice points (points with integer coordinates) (a, b) in the plane so that $a^2 + b^2 = n$. If there is such a point in any quadrant, there will another such in each of the other three quadrants.

In later problem sets, attention turns to the function S_2 defined at positive integers by $S_2(n) = \frac{s_2(2)}{4}$. There are several reasons for this, besides the convenience of dividing out by the common factor of 4 in the tabulation. One is that, unlike s_2, S_2 is *muliplicative*: $S_2(mn) = S_2(m)S_2(n)$ whenever m and n are relatively prime. Another has to do with arithmetic in the Gaussian integers $\mathbb{Z}[i]$, something we'll touch on briefly below (and see [5] for a detailed development).

Generating Functions

One of the themes in *FFNT* is the use of calculations with formal expressions to keep track of numerical data. A good example of this is perhaps the simplest one in the course: The coefficient of x^n in

$$(x + x^2 + x^3 + x^4 + x^5 + x^6)^k$$

is the number of ways you can roll a value of n if k dice are thrown.

Equivalently, it's the number of k-tuples of integers, each between 1 and 6, that sum to n.

On the surface, this seems a little amazing. The polynomial

$$x + x^2 + x^3 + x^4 + x^5 + x^6$$

is the generating function for the roll of one die: each of the integers between 1 and 6 can show up once, and no other integer can show up. When you square it, the coefficient of x^n is the number of ways n can be written as the sum of *two* integers between 1 and 6. And when you cube it, the coefficient of x^n is the number of ways n can be written as the sum of *three* integers between 1 and 6.

The reason that this works is because polynomial multiplication is tailor made for this kind of bookkeeping—it's the generalized distributive law. And counting, say, pairs of numbers between 1 and 6 that add to n involves exactly this kind of "each with each" calculation. So, there's a general principle here: if the coefficient of each x^n in a polynomial is the number of ways that n can be represented by some function, the coefficient if x^n in the kth power of that polynomial is number of ways that the n can be written as a sum of k values of that function.

This can be made precise, but in *FFNT* the principle is developed informally through examples. One of the most striking is used, together with a CAS, to generate values of s_2. If you want to count the number of ways an integer n is the sum of two squares, take a polynomial in which the coefficient of x^n is the number of ways n can be written as *one* square and multiply it by itself.

For example,
$9 = 3^2 = (-3)^2$.

But the number of ways a non-negative integer n can be written as a perfect square is

$$\begin{cases} 1 & \text{if } n = 0, \\ 0 & \text{if } n \text{ is not a perfect square, and} \\ 2 & \text{if } n \text{ is a perfect square} \end{cases}$$

So, if you want to look at s_2 for values between 0 and 49, build the polynomial

$$f(x) = 1 + 2x + 2x^4 + 2x^9 + 2x^{16} + 2x^{25} + 2x^{36} + 2x^{49}$$

The coefficient of x^n in $(f(x))^2$ for $0 \leqslant n \leqslant 49$ will be $s_2(n)$. And a CAS makes it easy to do the expansion; it reports the first fifty terms of $f(x)^2$:

Yes, a CAS helps reduce the computational overhead, but Jacobi calculated powers of this polynomial completely unplugged, around 1830. People had algebraic stamina back then.

$$\cdots + 4x^{49} + 8x^{45} + 8x^{41} + 8x^{40} + 8x^{37} + 4x^{36} + 8x^{34}$$
$$+ 4x^{32} + 8x^{29} + 8x^{26} + 12x^{25} + 8x^{20} + 4x^{18} + 8x^{17} + 4x^{16}$$
$$+ 8x^{13} + 8x^{10} + 4x^9 + 4x^8 + 8x^5 + 4x^4 + 4x^2 + 4x + 1$$

Ways to Think About It

The degree of $(f(x))^2$ is 98, and, in fact, the coefficient of x^n will be $s_2(n)$ up to $n = 63$ (why?), but then for $n \geqslant 64$ the coefficients will no longer be the appropriate values of s_2. We'd need to include more terms in f—what we really want is a power series.

This method leads to a tabulation of s_2 at integers n between 1 and 50:

n	$s_2(n)$	n	$s_2(n)$	n	$s_2(n)$	n	$s_2(n)$	n	$s_2(n)$
1	4	11	0	21	0	31	0	41	8
2	4	12	0	22	0	32	4	42	0
3	0	13	8	23	0	33	0	43	0
4	4	14	0	24	0	34	8	44	0
5	8	15	0	25	12	35	0	45	8
6	0	16	4	26	8	36	4	46	0
7	0	17	8	27	0	37	8	47	0
8	4	18	4	28	0	38	0	48	0
9	4	19	0	29	8	39	0	49	4
10	8	20	8	30	0	40	8	50	12

The Conjecture

The main use of the generating polynomial for s_2 in *FFNT* is to create tables like the one above. Let $S_2 = \frac{s_2}{4}$, and denote the parent of S_2 by χ, so that for $n \geqslant 1$,

$$S_2(n) = \sum_{d|n} \chi(d)$$

This condition is essentially a recurrence, so that $S_2(n)$ can be calculated if one knows the $S_2(m)$ for $m \leqslant n$ (in fact for $m \mid n$). So, for example, one can calculate like this:

$$1 = S_2(1) = \chi(1)$$
$$\text{so } \chi(1) = 1$$

$$1 = S_2(2) = \chi(1) + \chi(2)$$
$$= 1 + \chi(2), \quad \text{so } \chi(2) = 0$$

$$0 = S_2(3) = \chi(1) + \chi(3)$$
$$= 1 + \chi(3), \quad \text{so } \chi(3) = -1$$

$$1 = S_2(4) = \chi(1) + \chi(2) + \chi(4)$$
$$= 1 + (-1) + \chi(4), \quad \text{so } \chi(4) = 0$$

$$2 = S_2(5) = \chi(1) + \chi(5)$$
$$= 1 + \chi(5), \quad \text{so } \chi(5) = 1$$

$$0 = S_2(6) = \chi(1) + \chi(2) + \chi(3) + \chi(6)$$
$$= 1 + 0 + (-1) + \chi(6), \quad \text{so } \chi(6) = 0$$

$$0 = S_2(7) = \chi(1) + \chi(7)$$
$$= 1 + \chi(7), \quad \text{so } \chi(7) = -1$$

$$1 = S_2(8) = \chi(1) + \chi(2) + \chi(4) + \chi(8)$$
$$= 1 + 0 + 0 + \chi(8), \qquad \text{so } \chi(8) = 0$$

Continuing in this way, one can build up a table for χ from that of S_2. Along the way, conjectures arise about values of χ at, say, primes or even integers. The complete picture shows some clear regularity:

n	$S_2(n)$	$\chi(n)$	n	$S_2(n)$	$\chi(n)$	n	$S_2(n)$	$\chi(n)$
1	1	1	11	0	−1	21	0	1
2	1	0	12	0	0	22	0	0
3	0	−1	13	2	1	23	0	−1
4	1	0	14	0	0	24	0	0
5	2	1	15	0	−1	25	3	1
6	0	0	16	1	0	26	2	0
7	0	−1	17	2	1	27	0	−1
8	1	0	18	1	0	28	0	0
9	1	1	19	0	−1	29	2	1
10	2	0	20	2	0	30	0	0

n	$S_2(n)$	$\chi(n)$	n	$S_2(n)$	$\chi(n)$
31	0	−1	41	2	1
32	1	0	42	0	0
33	0	1	43	0	−1
34	2	0	44	0	0
35	0	−1	45	2	1
36	1	0	46	0	0
37	2	1	47	0	−1
38	0	0	48	0	0
39	0	−1	49	1	1
40	2	0	50	3	0

In the table, χ takes on values −1, 0, and 1. $\chi(n)$ is 0 if n is even, $\chi(n)$ is 1 if n is of form $4k + 1$, and $\chi(n)$ is −1 if n is of the form $4k + 3$. The evidence leads one to a conjecture:

Conjecture 4.1

If $\chi : \mathbb{N} \to \mathbb{C}$ is defined by

$$\chi(n) = \begin{cases} 0 & \text{if } n \text{ is even,} \\ 1 & \text{if } n \equiv 1 \bmod 4, \text{ and} \\ -1 & \text{if } n \equiv 3 \bmod 4 \end{cases}$$

then

$$S_2(n) = \sum_{d|n} \chi(d) \qquad \blacksquare \qquad (4)$$

Note that the sum on the right-hand side of this equation is the excess of the number of divisors of n of the form $4k + 1$ over those of form $4k + 3$. Hence, if the conjecture is true, we have a theorem, due to Fermat:

Theorem 4.2 (tentative)
Notation as above, for n a positive integer, $S_2(n)$ is the excess of the number of divisors of n of the form $4k + 1$ over those of form $4k + 3$.

Note also that the left-hand side of Equation (4) is non-negative. Hence, if the theorem is true, there are, for any positive integer n, at least as many divisors that are 1 mod 4 as there are that are 3 mod 4.

The Proof

Theorem 4.2 is a corollary of Conjecture 4.3. And one proof of Conjecture 4.3 uses many of the ideas developed in *FFNT*. For example, one way to show that

$$S_2(n) = \sum_{d|n} \chi(d)$$

is to use Theorem 4.1 and to show that

$$\zeta(s) \sum_{n=1}^{\infty} \frac{\chi(n)}{n^s} = \sum_{n=1}^{\infty} \frac{S_2(n)}{n^s} \qquad (5)$$

This looks like a good lead, but, in fact, Equation (5) just uses Theorem 4.1 to restate what we want to prove. It *is* useful, but only after we get some alternate formulas for S_2 and χ. A detailed development with complete proofs is in Chapter 8 of [5], but we give the main points here:

1. Multiplicative functions and the product expansion.

Some functions $a : \mathbb{C} \to \mathbb{C}$ have the property that they respect multiplication, in the sense that for positive integers m, n,

$$a(mn) = a(m)a(n)$$

Such functions are called ***multiplicative*** (or "strongly multiplicative"). Examples include $n \mapsto n^k$ and the function χ defined above (a fact that you can check). If a is multiplicative, there is a sum-to-product representation of the Dirichlet series $\sum_{n=1}^{\infty} \frac{a(n)}{n^s}$, a consequence of the fundamental theorem of arithmetic:

There are **weakly multiplicitive** functions, too. They satisfy $a(mn) = a(m)a(n)$ whenever m and n are relatively prime. We'll see that S_2 is weakly multiplicitive.

Theorem 4.3

If a is multiplicative, the Dirichlet series

$$\sum_{n=1}^{\infty} \frac{a(n)}{n^s}$$

can be expressed as

$$\prod_{p} \left(\frac{1}{1 - \frac{a(p)}{p^s}} \right) \tag{6}$$

where the product is over all prime numbers p.

Proof.

Each factor in expression (6) is a geometric series:

To be rigorous, we should put some restrictions on the values of $a(k)$ to ensure that the series converges.

$$\frac{1}{1 - \frac{a(p)}{p^s}} = 1 + \left(\frac{a(p)}{p^s} \right) + \left(\frac{a(p)}{p^s} \right)^2 + \left(\frac{a(p)}{p^s} \right)^3 + \dots$$

$$= 1 + \left(\frac{a(p)}{p^s} \right) + \left(\frac{a(p^2)}{p^{2s}} \right) + \left(\frac{a(p^3)}{p^{3s}} \right) + \dots$$

Multiply all these together (one for every prime) and you get the sum of every possible expression of the form:

$$\frac{a(p_1^{e_1})a(p_2^{e_2})\dots a(p_r^{e_r})}{p_1^{e_1 s}p_2^{e_2 s}\dots p_r^{e_r s}} = \frac{a(p_1^{e_1}p_2^{e_2}\dots p_r^{e_r})}{\left(p_1^{e_1}p_2^{e_2}\dots p_r^{e_r}\right)^s}$$

Since every $n \in \mathbb{Z}$ can be written in one and only one way as a product of powers of primes, this is the same as the sum

$$\sum_{n=1}^{\infty} \frac{a(n)}{n^s}$$

■

As examples, we have

$$\sum_{n=1}^{\infty} \frac{1}{n^s} = \prod_{p} \left(\frac{1}{1 - \frac{1}{p^s}} \right), \quad \text{and}$$

$$\sum_{n=1}^{\infty} \frac{\chi(n)}{n^s} = \prod_{p} \left(\frac{1}{1 - \frac{\chi(p)}{p^s}} \right)$$

So, we can express Conjecture 4.1 (via equation 5) as

Conjecture 4.2 (Conjecture 4.1, restated)

$$\prod_{p} \left(\frac{1}{1 - \frac{1}{p^s}} \right) \prod_{p} \left(\frac{1}{1 - \frac{\chi(p)}{p^s}} \right) = \sum_{n=1}^{\infty} \frac{S_2(n)}{n^s} \tag{7}$$

2. S_2 and Gaussian integers.

We're looking at the number of ways an integer can be expressed integrally as $a^2 + b^2$. If we move up to the complex numbers,

$$a^2 + b^2 = (a + bi)(a - bi).$$

So, for $n \geqslant 1$, $s_2(n)$ is the number of complex numbers z with integer real and imaginary parts such that $z\bar{z} = n$, and $S_2(n)$ is one fourth of this number.

If $z = a + bi, \bar{z} = a - bi$, the complex conjugate of z.

The function N defined on $\mathbb{C}$ by $N(z) = z\bar{z}$ is called the *norm*, and it has some important properties:

1. If $z = a + bi$, $N(z) = N(\bar{z}) = a^2 + b^2$.

2. $N(z)$ is a non-negative real number, and $N(z) = 0$ if and only if $z = 0$.

3. N is multiplicative: $N(zw) = N(z)N(w)$ for all complex numbers z and w.

The proofs of these facts amount to generic calculations, and the details are in [5].

The complex numbers with integer real and imaginary parts form a ring $\mathbb{Z}[i]$ called the ring of *Gaussian integers*. $\mathbb{Z}[i]$ shares many structural properties with the ordinary integers $\mathbb{Z}$: There's a division algorithm, a Euclidean algorithm, and unique factorization into primes.

$\mathbb{Z}[i]$ is the set of all lattice points in the complex plane.

Ways to Think About It

Unique factorization means that every element can be written as a product of prime elements in "essentially one way." In $\mathbb{Z}$, this means there's only one prime factorization of an integer if you ignore the order in which the factors are listed and the insertion of unit factors of 1 and -1. It's the same with $\mathbb{Z}[i]$, except there are more unit factors to consider: The only elements of $\mathbb{Z}[i]$ whose reciprocals are also in $\mathbb{Z}[i]$ a are 1, -1, i, and $-i$. So, a prime factorization of 2 in $\mathbb{Z}[i]$ is $(1 - i)^2$ because $1 - i$ is a prime in $\mathbb{Z}[i]$ and

$$2 = (-i)(1 - i)^2$$

Put another way, two Gaussian integers that are unit multiples of each other generate the same ideal in $\mathbb{Z}[i]$.

Two Gaussian integers that are unit multiples of each other are called *associates*.

So, another way to think about $s_2(n)$ is *the number of Gaussian integers of norm n*. And, if we define the first quadrant Q_1 like this:

$$Q_1 = \{z = a + bi \in \mathbb{C} \mid a > 0, b \geqslant 0\},$$

we have another way to state the definition of S_2: $S_2(n)$ is the number of Gaussian integers in Q_1 with norm n. In

Note that we are excluding 0 from Q_1.

symbols,

$$S_2(n) = |\{z \in \mathbb{Z}[i] \mid N(z) = n \text{ and } z \in Q_1\}|$$

So, the right-hand side of Equation (5)

$$\sum_{n=1}^{\infty} \frac{S_2(n)}{n^s}$$

can be written in another way: Each term in the sum is a sum of unit fractions, and the number of such fractions is the number of Gaussian integers with given norm. For example, the $\dfrac{3}{25^s}$ comes from

$$\frac{1}{N(3+4i)} + \frac{1}{N(4+3i)} + \frac{1}{N(5+0i)}$$

Using this idea and the mutiplicitivity of N, we get a product formula for the right-hand side to Equation (5):

$$\sum_{n=1}^{\infty} \frac{S_2(n)}{n^s} = \sum_{\alpha \in Q_1} \frac{1}{(N(\alpha))^s}$$

The right side is called the **Dedekind zeta function** for $\mathbb{Z}[i]$.

$$= \prod_{p \in Q_1} \sum_{k=0}^{\infty} \frac{1}{\left((N(p))^k\right)^s} \qquad \text{(use the fundamental theorem in } \mathbb{Z}[i])$$

$$= \prod_{p \in Q_1} \frac{1}{1 - \frac{1}{N(p)^s}} \qquad \text{(sum a geometric series)}$$

Here, the product is over all Gaussian primes in the first quadrant. This is another example of a calculation that is best understood by working it out.

Putting together the pieces, we get a form of Conjecture 4.1 that can be used to prove it:

Conjecture 4.3 (Conjecture 4.2, restated)

$$\prod_{p} \left(\frac{1}{1 - \frac{1}{p^s}} \right) \prod_{p} \left(\frac{1}{1 - \frac{\chi(p)}{p^s}} \right) = \prod_{p \in Q_1} \frac{1}{1 - \frac{1}{N(p)^s}} \qquad (8)$$

We've converted a conjecture about sums to a conjecture about products. The last step is to dig into the right-hand side in order to transform it into the left-hand side.

3. Law of decomposition.

One of the most beautiful aspects of the structure of $\mathbb{Z}[i]$ is the classification of its primes. Some ordinary primes like 5 are no longer primes in the Gaussian integers; they **split** into two distinct prime factors ($5 = (2 + i)(2 - i)$). Other primes like 7 stay prime (they are **inert**) even when you look at them in this larger setting. And the prime 2 exhibits a special behavior called **ramification**—it is essentially the square of $1 - i$, because $2 = -i(1 - i)^2$. And these are the only three kinds of decomposition when you move from $\mathbb{Z}$ to $\mathbb{Z}[i]$.

How can you tell how an ordinary prime will behave when you move up to $\mathbb{Z}[i]$. Remarkably, there's a simple test that can be carried out inside $\mathbb{Z}$ that will tell you exactly what happens. Here are the details, without proof (again, see [5] for details):

Theorem 4.4

Every prime p in $\mathbb{Z}$ does one of three things when you move up to $\mathbb{Z}[i]$:

- *It can* split *into two (conjugate) factors:*

$$p = \mathfrak{p}\overline{\mathfrak{p}}$$

The primes in $\mathbb{Z}[i]$ that enter into the decomposition of the prime p in $\mathbb{Z}$ are said to **lie above** p.

- *It can remain* inert, *staying prime in $\mathbb{Z}[i]$.*

- *It can* ramify *into the square of a prime in $\mathbb{Z}[i]$:*

$$p = \mathfrak{p}^2$$

Furthermore, we have the following decomposition law *to tell which is which:*

- *p splits* $\Leftrightarrow p \equiv 1 \pmod 4$

- *p is inert* $\Leftrightarrow p \equiv 3 \pmod 4$

- *p ramifies* $\Leftrightarrow p = 2$

This theorem was generalized independently in the 1920s by Artin and Takagi.

The decomposition law looks upstairs from $\mathbb{Z}$ to $\mathbb{Z}[i]$. We can also look downstairs from $\mathbb{Z}[i]$ to $\mathbb{Z}$, in a form that is especially useful for the next calculation:

Theorem 4.5

Every prime in Q_1 lies above one of these:

- *the prime 2. There's just one: $1 + i$, and $N(1 + i) = 2$*

- a prime p *that is congruent to 1 mod 4. There are two for each such* p—*if*

$$p = \mathfrak{p}\,\bar{\mathfrak{p}},$$

  then both $\mathfrak{p}$ *and* $\bar{\mathfrak{p}}$ *have an associate in* Q_1 *(and they are different), and each has norm* p.

- a prime p *that is congruent to 3 mod 4. There's only one such prime in* Q_1, *because such a* p *is inert, and* $N(\mathfrak{p}) = p^2$.

The decomposition law allows us to derive Equation (8)

4. The calculation.

Remember, we want to show that

$$\prod_{p} \left(\frac{1}{1 - \frac{1}{p^s}} \right) \prod_{p} \left(\frac{1}{1 - \frac{\chi(p)}{p^s}} \right) = \prod_{\mathfrak{p} \in Q_1} \frac{1}{1 - \frac{1}{N(\mathfrak{p})^s}}$$

Using the results so far—especially the result of Theorem 4.5 and the facts that χ is 0 on even integers, the calculation goes like this:

$$\prod_{z \in Q_1} \frac{1}{1 - \frac{1}{N(z)^s}} = \frac{1}{1 - \frac{1}{2^s}} \left(\prod_{p \equiv 1 \bmod 4} \frac{1}{1 - \frac{1}{p^s}} \right)^2 \left(\prod_{p \equiv 3 \bmod 4} \frac{1}{1 - \frac{1}{p^{2s}}} \right)$$

$$= \frac{1}{1 - \frac{1}{2^s}} \left(\prod_{p \equiv 1 \bmod 4} \frac{1}{1 - \frac{1}{p^s}} \right)^2 \left(\prod_{p \equiv 3 \bmod 4} \frac{1}{1 - \frac{1}{p^s}} \right) \left(\prod_{p \equiv 3 \bmod 4} \frac{1}{1 + \frac{1}{p^s}} \right)$$

$$= \frac{1}{1 - \frac{1}{2^s}} \left(\prod_{p \text{ odd}} \frac{1}{1 - \frac{1}{p^s}} \right) \left(\prod_{p \equiv 1 \bmod 4} \frac{1}{1 - \frac{1}{p^s}} \right) \left(\prod_{p \equiv 3 \bmod 4} \frac{1}{1 + \frac{1}{p^s}} \right)$$

$$= \left(\prod_{p} \frac{1}{1 - \frac{1}{p^s}} \right) \left(\prod_{p \equiv 1 \bmod 4} \frac{1}{1 - \frac{\chi(p)}{p^s}} \right) \left(\prod_{p \equiv 3 \bmod 4} \frac{1}{1 - \frac{\chi(p)}{p^s}} \right)$$

$$= \left(\prod_{p} \frac{1}{1 - \frac{1}{p^s}} \right) \left(\prod_{p} \frac{1}{1 - \frac{\chi(p)}{p^s}} \right)$$

This establishes (granting all that we've assumed) Conjecture 4.3 and hence Fermat's Theorem 4.2.

Bonus Results and Further Results

Several results follow from Theorem 4.2. We've already mention one: Since

$$S_2(n) = \sum_{d \mid n} \chi(d)$$

and since the left-hand side is non-negative, so is the right-had side, and hence *every integer has at least as many divisors of form* $4k + 1$ *as it has of form* $4k + 3$.

Another result, one that is experimentally conjectured and proved in *FFNT* (and in many workshops we've been in with teachers) comes from a general result about multiplicative functions: The child of a multiplicative function is weakly multiplicative (see Chapter 1 of [2] for a proof). In particular, if m and n are relatively prime,

$$S_2(mn) = S_2(m)S_2(n)$$

This implies that we only need to look at values of S_2 at prime powers, and a beautiful formula for this (and a generalization to S_2's family tree) evolves in the problem sets.

If you tabulate S_2, the results seem to be erratic. When this happens, it's useful to look at its average value. Using s_2 rather than S_2, there's a beautiful result, due to Gauss and developed over the problem sets, that shows that

$$\lim_{n \to \infty} \frac{1}{n} \sum_{k=1}^{n} s_2(k) = \pi$$

Essentially, $\sum_{k=1}^{n} s_2(k)$ counts the lattice points (a, b) such that $a^2 + b^2 \leqslant n$. These are the lattice points on or interior to a circle of radius $\sqrt{n}$. For large n, this approximates the area of this circle, which is πn. The complete proof is in [1].

Finally, the same program is used in *FFNT* to conjecture a formula for $s_4(n)$, the number or ways an integer cane written as a sum of four squares. One uses the coefficients of

$$(1 + 2x + 2x^4 + 2x^9 + \ldots)^4$$

to generate data and then, one by one, calculates the values of the parent function. The result again jumps out of

What about carrying out this program for the cube of the polynomial (and hence the representations as a sum of three squares)? Try it.

the calculations: $s_4(n)$ seems to be eight times the sum of the positive divisors of n that are not divisible by 4. See [3] for a proof.

Bibliography

[1] Andrews, G. *Number Theory*. Dover, New York, 1994.

[2] Apostol, T. *Analytic Number Theory*, Springer Verlag, New York, 1976.

[3] Berndt, B.C. *Number Theory in the Spirit of Ramanujan*, AMS, Providence, 2006.

[4] Cuoco, A. *Investigations in Algebra*, MIT Press, Cambridge MA, 1990.

[5] Cuoco, A., and Joseph J. Rotman. *Learning Modern Algebra*, MAA, Washington DC, 2013.

[6] Cuoco, A. "Searching for Möbius", College Mathematics Journal, 37:2, 148–153.

[7] EDC. *CME Project*. Pearson, Boston MA, 2013.

[8] Ireland, K. and Rosen, M. *A Classical Introduction to Modern Number Theory* Springer-Verlag, 1991.

[9] Wilf, H., *Generatingfunctionology*, Academic Press, New York, 1994.

CHAPTER

5 Solutions

Problem Set 1

Opener

n	1	2	3	4	5	6	7	8	9	10	11	12
$\sigma(n)$	1	3	4	7	6	12	8	15	13	18	12	28

n	13	14	15	16	17	18	19	20	21	22	23	24
$\sigma(n)$	14	24	24	31	18	39	20	42	32	36	24	60

n	25	26	27	28	29	30	31	32	33	34	35	36
$\sigma(n)$	31	42	40	56	30	72	32	63	48	54	48	91

n	37	38	39	40	41	42	43	44	45	46	47	48
$\sigma(n)$	38	60	56	90	42	96	44	84	78	72	48	124

n	49	50	51	52	53	54	55	56	57	58	59	60
$\sigma(n)$	57	93	72	98	54	120	72	120	80	90	60	168

n	61	62	63	64	65	66	67	68	69	70	71	72
$\sigma(n)$	62	96	104	127	84	144	68	126	96	144	72	195

n	73	74	75	76	77	78	79	80	81	82	83	84
$\sigma(n)$	74	114	124	140	96	168	80	186	121	126	84	224

n	85	86	87	88	89	90	91	92	93	94	95	96
$\sigma(n)$	108	132	120	180	90	234	112	168	128	144	120	252

Example: $\sigma(81) = 1 + 3 + 9 + 27 + 81 = 121$. Note that we add 9 once even though $9^2 = 81$.

1. There are many interesting patterns that hold for the σ function. A couple of these patterns are pointed out in the "Neat Stuff" section of this problem set (see Problems 4–6). To name a few particularly useful/interesting patterns, we see:

   - $\sigma(p) = p + 1$ for any prime p. This is further discussed in Problem 4.
   - More generally, $\sigma(p^c) = 1 + p + p^2 + \cdots + p^c$ where p is a prime. Using a bit of algebra, we note that $(1 + p + \cdots + p^c)(p - 1) = (p^{c+1} - 1)$. Thus, we could more simply write

   $$\sigma(p^c) = \frac{p^{c+1} - 1}{p - 1}.$$

   - $\sigma(ab) = \sigma(a)\sigma(b)$ if a and b are numbers that share no common factors aside from 1. This is a particularly useful pattern when dealing with large numbers with lots of factors. The special case where a and b are prime is further explored in problem 5–6.
   - Combining the previous two facts, we can actually find an alternative formula for $\sigma(n)$. In particular, if $n = p_1^{a_1} p_2^{a_2} \cdots p_k^{a_k}$, we know that

   $$\sigma(n) = \frac{p_1^{a_1+1} - 1}{p_1 - 1} \frac{p_2^{a_2+1} - 1}{p_2 - 1} \cdots \frac{p_k^{a_k+1} - 1}{p_k - 1}.$$

2. We solve these as follows:

   a. $\sigma(128) = 255$.
   We can compute this in two ways. First, we could just sum up the factors to yield

   $$\sigma(128) = 1 + 2 + 4 + 8 + 16 + 32 + 64 + 128 = 255.$$

   Alternatively, using our formula from number 1, we see that

   $$\sigma(128) = \frac{2^8 - 1}{2 - 1} = 256 - 1 = 255.$$

   b. $\sigma(243) = 364$
   By similar logic to part a, we see that

   $$\sigma(243) = 1 + 3 + 9 + 27 + 81 + 243 = 364$$

   or

   $$\sigma(243) = \frac{3^6 - 1}{3 - 1} = \frac{728}{2} = 364.$$

   c. $\sigma(5 \cdot 49) = 342$

Here we can either multiply out $5 \cdot 49$ to yield

$$\sigma(245) = 1 + 5 + 7 + 35 + 49 + 245 = 342$$

or by noticing 5 and 49 share no common factors, apply our formula from part a to reduce the problem

$$\sigma(5 \cdot 49) = \sigma(5) \cdot \sigma(49) = 6 \cdot 57 = 342.$$

d. $\sigma(257) = 258$

257 is a prime number, so $\sigma(257) = 258$.

e. $\sigma(1001) = 1344$

We can list out all factors of 1001 to yield

$$\sigma(1001) = 1 + 7 + 11 + 13 + 77 + 91 + 143 + 1001$$
$$= 1344.$$

Alternatively, we could note that $1001 = 7 \cdot 11 \cdot 13$. Then since $7, 11,$ and 13 are all prime, we can compute

$$\sigma(1001) = \sigma(7) \cdot \sigma(11) \cdot \sigma(13) = 8 \cdot 12 \cdot 14 = 1344.$$

3. (a) If $n > 1$, then $1, n$ are distinct divisors of n, and so if we drop all of the other divisors of n in the expression for $\sigma(n)$, we find that $A(n) \geqslant \frac{n+1}{n} > 1$. So $n > 1$ does not work. It can be checked $n = 1$ works, so $n = 1$ is the only solution.

   (b) The three smallest such numbers are 6, 28, 496.

   (c) It turns out that $n = 120$ is a solution to $A(n) = 3$.

   How might we find such a solution without brute force? First, it helps to know the two main properties of the σ function, that $A(m)A(n) = A(mn)$ for relatively prime m, n, and $A(p^k) = \frac{p^{k+1}-1}{p^k(p-1)}$ for p prime and k a positive integer. One can then write down the values of $A(p^k)$ for various small p (7 or less) and some small values for k. Prime factorize the numerators and denominators of the values you get, and play around with combining the fractions so that all of the prime factors cancel except for a 3.

   $$A(2^3)A(3^1)A(5^1)$$

   turns out to work, which corresponds to $A(120)$.

Neat Stuff

4. Notice in the table that the primes all have a peculiar relationship with their $\sigma(p)$. If p is prime, then $\sigma(p) = p + 1$. Also since $A(n) = \frac{\sigma(n)}{n}$, $A(p) = \frac{p+1}{p} = 1 + \frac{1}{p}$.

5. If p and q are primes, then $\sigma(pq) = (1+p)(1+q)$. Also, $A(pq) = 1 + \frac{1}{p} + \frac{1}{q} + \frac{1}{pq}$.

6. The maximum possible value of $A(pq)$ comes from when p and q are as small as possible. Thus if we consider $p = 2$ and $q = 3$, we have that

$$A(2 \cdot 3) = 1 + \frac{1}{2} + \frac{1}{3} + \frac{1}{2 \cdot 3}$$
$$= 2.$$

Problem Set 2

Opener

n	1	2	3	4	5	6	7	8	9	10	11	12
$a(n)$	1	$\frac{3}{2}$	$\frac{4}{3}$	$\frac{7}{4}$	$\frac{6}{5}$	2	$\frac{8}{7}$	$\frac{15}{8}$	$\frac{13}{9}$	$\frac{9}{5}$	$\frac{12}{11}$	$\frac{7}{3}$

n	13	14	15	16	17	18	19	20	21	22	23	24
$a(n)$	$\frac{14}{13}$	$\frac{12}{7}$	$\frac{8}{5}$	$\frac{31}{16}$	$\frac{18}{17}$	$\frac{13}{6}$	$\frac{20}{19}$	$\frac{21}{10}$	$\frac{32}{21}$	$\frac{18}{11}$	$\frac{24}{23}$	$\frac{5}{2}$

n	25	26	27	28	29	30	31	32	33	34	35	36
$a(n)$	$\frac{31}{25}$	$\frac{21}{13}$	$\frac{40}{27}$	2	$\frac{30}{29}$	$\frac{12}{5}$	$\frac{32}{31}$	$\frac{63}{32}$	$\frac{16}{11}$	$\frac{27}{17}$	$\frac{48}{35}$	$\frac{91}{36}$

n	37	38	39	40	41	42	43	44	45	46	47	48
$a(n)$	$\frac{38}{37}$	$\frac{30}{19}$	$\frac{56}{39}$	$\frac{9}{4}$	$\frac{42}{41}$	$\frac{16}{7}$	$\frac{44}{43}$	$\frac{21}{11}$	$\frac{26}{15}$	$\frac{36}{23}$	$\frac{48}{47}$	$\frac{31}{12}$

1. Most of these answers can be calculated from the table we've filled out.

   (a) $a(3) \cdot a(4) = \frac{7}{3}$.
   (b) $a(2) \cdot a(5) = \frac{9}{5}$.
   (c) $a(8) \cdot a(15) = 3$.

    (d) $a(120) = 3$. This should be calculated directly, but note that it is the same value as $a(8) \cdot a(15)$.

    (e) $a(10) \cdot a(12) = \frac{21}{5}$. Note that this is *not* the same value as $a(8) \cdot a(15)$, nor is it equal to $a(120)$. This problem hints at the appropriate definition for multiplicative functions.

2. The key thing here is to identify the sums of reciprocals as an expanded representation of various $a(n)$, and almost all the answers are the same as the previous problem.

    (a) $\left(1 + \frac{1}{3}\right)\left(1 + \frac{1}{2} + \frac{1}{4}\right) = a(3) \cdot a(4) = \frac{7}{3}$.

    (b) $\left(1 + \frac{1}{2}\right)\left(1 + \frac{1}{5}\right) = a(2) \cdot a(5) = \frac{9}{5}$.

    (c) $\left(1 + \frac{1}{2} + \frac{1}{4} + \frac{1}{8}\right)\left(1 + \frac{1}{3} + \frac{1}{5} + \frac{1}{15}\right) = a(8) \cdot a(15) = 3$.

    (d) $\left(1 + \frac{1}{2} + \frac{1}{5} + \frac{1}{10}\right)\left(1 + \frac{1}{2} + \frac{1}{3} + \frac{1}{4} + \frac{1}{6} + \frac{1}{12}\right) = a(10) \cdot a(12) = \frac{21}{5}$. Note again this is *not* the same answer as the previous part.

3. All summations evaluate to $\frac{2^{n+1}-1}{2^n}$, where n is the highest power of 2 in the summation. Also notice that as the number of terms in the summation increase, the value gets closer and closer to 2, which you can also notice by rewriting the sum as $2 - \frac{1}{2^n}$.

    (a) $1 + \frac{1}{2} = \frac{3}{2}$.

    (b) $1 + \frac{1}{2} + \frac{1}{4} = \frac{7}{4}$.

    (c) $\frac{1}{2^0} + \frac{1}{2^1} + \frac{1}{2^2} + \frac{1}{2^3} = \frac{15}{8}$.

    (d) $\frac{1}{2^0} + \frac{1}{2^1} + \frac{1}{2^2} + \cdots + \frac{1}{2^6} = \frac{127}{64}$.

    (e) The phrase: "the sum of all numbers in the form $\frac{1}{2^n}$ as n goes from 0 to 10" can be mathematically represented as the sum:

$$\frac{1}{2^0} + \frac{1}{2^1} + \frac{1}{2^2} + \cdots + \frac{1}{2^{10}} = \frac{2047}{1024}.$$

    (f) $\displaystyle\sum_{n=0}^{11} \frac{1}{2^n} = \frac{4095}{2048}$.

    (g) $\displaystyle\sum_{n=0}^{\infty} \frac{1}{2^n} = 2$.

4. We note first that $a(n)$ is exactly the same as $A(n) = \sigma(n)/n$ from Problem Set 1. Recall from Set 1 problem 1 that we derived

$$\sigma(p^c) = \frac{p^{c+1} - 1}{p - 1}$$

where p is prime. Here we are considering powers of 3. Using this formula, we can determine

$$a(3^c) = \frac{\sigma(3^c)}{3^c}$$

$$= \frac{\frac{3^{c+1}-1}{2}}{3^c}$$

$$= \frac{3^{c+1}-1}{2 \cdot 3^c}$$

$$= \frac{3}{2} - \frac{1}{3^c}$$

This means we want to determine a k such that $k > 3/2 - 1/3^c$ for any integer value $c > 0$. Notice that as c grows, $1/3^c$ gets smaller and smaller, and thus the quantity $3/2 - 1/3^c$ gets larger and larger. Taking the limit as c goes to infinity, the $1/3^c$ term goes to zero, so the quantity becomes essentially $3/2$.

Thus, picking $k = 3/2$ will ensure $k > a(n)$ for all powers of 3.

Neat Stuff

5. For $3 + n/2 + n$ to be an integer we require n to be even. We can also check manually that $n > 4$. So $1, 2, n/2, n$ are distinct divisors of n. The sum of these turns out to be $3 + n/2 + n$, so it turns out these are all of the divisors of n. The only numbers with four divisors are those of the form p^3 or pq for distinct primes p, q. Here we need n to be even, so the possible solutions are 8 and $2p$ for any prime p.

   A generalization is to ask for the solutions to $\sigma(n) = 1 + p + n/p + n$ for a fixed prime p. An argument similar to the above shows that all solutions are p^3 and pq for any prime $q \neq p$.

6. We assume p, q are distinct. The divisors of pq are $1, p, q, pq$. So

   $$\sigma(pq) = 1 + p + q + pq = (p+1)(q+1).$$

   Notice that $\sigma(p) = p + 1$ and $\sigma(q) = q + 1$, so that $\sigma(pq) = \sigma(p)\sigma(q)$.

7. We assume p, q are distinct. The divisors of pq are $1, p, q, pq$. So

$$a(pq) = 1 + \frac{1}{p} + \frac{1}{q} + \frac{1}{pq} = \left(1 + \frac{1}{p}\right)\left(1 + \frac{1}{q}\right) = \frac{(p+1)(q+1)}{pq}$$

8. (a) If $n = 2^x 3^y$, then using the patterns observed in problems 2 and 3, we can find that

$$a(2^x 3^y) = a(2^x)a(3^y) = \frac{2^{x+1}-1}{2^x(2-1)} \cdot \frac{3^{y+1}-1}{3^y(3-1)}.$$

It can be checked that this increases as x, y increases. So to find an upper bound, we take x, y to infinity. We find

$$\lim_{x \to \infty} \frac{2^{x+1}-1}{2^x(2-1)} = 2, \qquad \lim_{y \to \infty} \frac{3^{y+1}-1}{3^y(3-1)} = \frac{3}{2}.$$

So $a(2^x 3^y) < 2 \cdot \frac{3}{2} = 3$, and this is the smallest possible number.

(b) The smallest possible number is $2^5 3^3 = 864$.

9. The first 10 numerators of the given expansion are $1, 3, 4, 7, 6, 12, 8, 15, 13, 18$. Referencing our table from Problem Set 1, we note that these numbers are exactly $\sigma(n)$ where n^x is the denominator corresponding to the numerator $\sigma(n)$. We can actually prove that this is, in fact, always the case!

Consider some arbitrary denominator n^x in the expansion. Let d be a divisor of n. Then d^x evenly divides n^x. This implies that there is some integer n/d, so there must be a fraction d/d^x in the first term and a $1/(n/d)^x$ in the second term. When we multiply these terms together, we obtain d/n^x, so this adds d to the numerator of our n^x term.

Since this holds true for every divisor d of n, the numerator of n^x in our expansion will end up being the sum of the divisors of n, which by definition is exactly $\sigma(n)$.

10. The first 10 numerators of the given expansion are $1, 5, 10, 21, 26, 50, 50, 85, 91, 130$. Referencing our table from Problem Set 1, we note that these numbers are exactly $\sigma_2(n)$ where n^x is the denominator corresponding to the numerator $\sigma_2(n)$. By a proof similar to problem 9 of this Set, we can show that this will always be the case.

Consider some arbitrary denominator n^x in the expansion. Let d be a divisor of n. Then d^x evenly divides n^x. This implies that there is some integer n/d, so there must be a fraction d^2/d^x in the first term and a $1/(n/d)^x$ in the second term. When we multiply these terms together, we obtain d^2/n^x, so this adds d^2 to the numerator of our n^x term.

Since this holds true for every divisor d of n, the numerator of n^x in our expansion will end up being the sum of the squares of the divisors of n, which by definition is exactly $\sigma_2(n)$.

Problem Set 3

Opener

n	1	2	3	4	5	6	7	8	9	10	11	12
$k(n)$	1	3	5	8	9	15	13	20	21	27	21	40

n	13	14	15	16	17	18	19	20	21	22	23	24
$k(n)$	25	39	45	48	33	63	37	72	65	63	45	100

1. Answers will vary, but participants should notice that $k(n)$ has the same properties around multiplication that the functions did in Problem Sets 1 and 2: for example, $k(2) \cdot k(5) = k(10)$. For prime p, $k(p) = 2p + 1$ because only the boundary will have zeros.

2.   a. Since 8 and 15 don't share any divisors besides 1, if a number X is a multiple of both 8 and 15, then $X = 8 \cdot 15 \cdot n$ for some integer n. If we simplify this, we observe that $X = 120 \cdot n$. Thus we can conclude that the number X is also a multiple of 120 as well.

  b. No, Jennifer is not quite right. Here's a counterexample: the number 60. Notice that 60 is a multiple of both 10 and 12 ($6 \cdot 10 = 5 \cdot 12 = 60$), however 60 is not a multiple of 120. The distinction between this case and the previous one in part (a) is that 10 and 12 share a common divisor other than 1, namely the number 2. Due to this common divisor, we cannot say with certainty that if a number is a multiple of 10 and 12, then it must be a multiple of 120.

3. While checking just the units digits cannot confirm for us that the entire multiplication has been done correctly, it can in some cases tell us that the result is incorrect without the full multiplication. The units digit of the product is determined only by the units digit of the two numbers being multiplied.

   a. The units digit of $4 \times 3 = 12$ is 2, a match.
   b. The units digit of $7 \times 1 = 7$ is 7, a match.
   c. The units digit of $3 \times 5 = 15$ is 5, a match.
   d. The units digit of $8 \times 3 = 24$ is 4, which *does not match* the multiplication, so this must be the incorrect fact.

4. a. We can compute $4 \times 3 = 12$. The remainder of this when divided by 10 is 2, so 4×3 is congruent mod 10 to 2.
   b. We can compute $8 \times 3 = 24$. The remainder of this when divided by 10 is 4, so 8×3 is congruent mod 10 to 4.
   c. We can compute $8 \times 3 = 24$. The remainder of this when divided by 12 is 0, so 8×3 is congruent mod 12 to 0.
   d. We can make a table of values to help us solve this problem.

x	0	1	2	3	4	5	6	7	8
$2x$	0	2	4	6	8	10	12	14	16
$2x \bmod 9$	0	2	4	6	8	1	3	5	7

   From this we see that the solution to $2x = 7$ in mod 9 is $x = 8$.
   e. Again we will make a table of values to help us determine the solution.

x	0	1	2	3	4	5	6	7	8
x^2	0	1	4	9	16	25	36	49	64
$x^2 \bmod 9$	0	1	4	0	7	7	0	4	1

   From this we see that the solutions to $x^2 = 7$ in mod 9 are $x = 4$ and $x = 5$.

5. As we take more and more terms, the summation continues to grow though the rate of growth slows down. There is no maximum value of the sum.

   To see this, we can group together all terms with the same denominator. We notice that a fraction with denominator 2^k is repeated 2^{k-1} times for $k \geqslant 1$. But this means that when we sum all these terms together, we get

$$\underbrace{\frac{1}{2^k} + \cdots + \frac{1}{2^k}}_{2^{k-1} \text{ of these}} = 2^{k-1}\frac{1}{2^k} = \frac{1}{2}.$$

Since this is true for any $k \geqslant 1$, this means that at any point in the summation we can always find some number of terms to add on that will increase the value of the sum by at least $1/2$. Thus there is no maximum value of the sum.

6. a. So far in this course we have seen several multiplicative functions. As discussed in Problem Set 1 problem 1, both $\sigma(n)$ and $\sigma_2(n)$ are multiplicative function. Additionally in Problem Set 2 we found that $a(n)$ was multiplicative as well. Finally in this Set in problem 1 we discuss that $k(n)$ also has this property.

    b. Many simple functions turn out to be multiplicative. Some examples are $f(x) = 1$ and $f(x) = x^n$ for any positive integer n. The $\tau(n)$ function mentioned in problem 9 of this problem set turns out to be multiplicative, and as this course progresses we will encounter many many more multiplicative functions as well.

Neat Stuff

7. Here we will use the formula for an infinite geometric series whose first term is 1: $S = \frac{1}{1-r}$, where S is the value of the series and r is the ratio between any term and its predecessor. For the first four parts the ratios are $r = \frac{1}{2}$ through $r = \frac{1}{5}$. Note that while the notation is different in each statement, they mean the same thing, so part of the purpose of this problem is to get familiar with the notation involved.

    The formula for part (e) is not always true, because the sum only exists when the ratio of consecutive terms must be less than 1. The infinite series $\sum_{n=0}^{\infty} \frac{1}{p^n}$ only equals $\frac{p}{p-1}$ if $|p| > 1$. Otherwise the series doesn't actually sum (i.e. converge) to anything: try it with $p = \frac{1}{2}$ and see what happens!

8. a. Recall that from Problem Set 2, the function $a(n)$ returns the sum of the reciprocals of the

divisors of n. Thus

$$a(72) = 1+\frac{1}{2}+\frac{1}{3}+\frac{1}{4}+\frac{1}{6}+\frac{1}{8}+\frac{1}{9}+\frac{1}{12}+\frac{1}{18}+\frac{1}{24}+\frac{1}{36}+\frac{1}{72} = \frac{195}{72}.$$

b. From the table, we filled in during Problem Set 2, we have that $a(8) = \frac{15}{8}$ and $a(9) = \frac{13}{9}$. Thus,

$$a(8) \cdot a(9) = \frac{195}{72}.$$

c. Notice that by definition, the left sum of reciprocals is $a(8)$ while the right sum is $a(9)$. Thus, their product is the same as part (b): $\frac{195}{72}$.

d. When we expand the expression from part (c), we obtain the following sum:

$$1+\frac{1}{2}+\frac{1}{3}+\frac{1}{4}+\frac{1}{6}+\frac{1}{8}+\frac{1}{9}+\frac{1}{12}+\frac{1}{18}+\frac{1}{24}+\frac{1}{36}+\frac{1}{72}.$$

This expansion is exactly what we found $a(72)$ to be in part (a). Generalizing this argument can lead to a proof that $a(n)$ is a multiplicative function.

9. a.

n	1	2	3	4	5	6	7	8	9	10
$\tau(n)$	1	2	2	3	2	4	2	4	3	4
n	11	12	13	14	15	16	17	18	19	20
$\tau(n)$	2	6	2	4	4	5	2	6	2	6

(b) The function $\tau(n)$ is multiplicative. To prove this, suppose that a and b share no common factor larger than 1. Then if we compare the list of factors for a with the list of factors for b, then we expect to find no common number in these two lists (besides 1 that is) by our selection of a and b. If we arrange the lists such that the factors of a are along a row and the factors of b are along a column, we can create a table by multiplying a factor of a above and a factor of b from the side. The entries of this table together form a complete list of the factors of ab. Hence, $\tau(a) \cdot \tau(b) = \tau(ab)$ and thus τ is multiplicative.

(c) To calculate $\tau(n)$ for any positive integer n, we begin by decomposing n into its prime factorization. From here we can combinatorially find $\tau(n)$ by adding one to each exponent and multiplying the resulting exponents. For example $60 = 2^2 \cdot 3^1 \cdot 5^1$. Hence $\tau(60) = (2+1) \cdot (1+1) \cdot (1+1) = 12$.

10. If $n = 2^x 3^y$, then using the patterns observed in Problem Set 2 problems 2 and 3, we can find that

$$a(2^x 3^y) = a(2^x)a(3^y) = \frac{2^{x+1} - 1}{2^x(2-1)} \cdot \frac{3^{y+1} - 1}{3^y(3-1)}.$$

It can be checked that this increases as x, y increases. So to find an upper bound, we take x, y to infinity. We find

$$\lim_{x \to \infty} \frac{2^{x+1} - 1}{2^x(2-1)} = 2, \qquad \lim_{y \to \infty} \frac{3^{y+1} - 1}{3^y(3-1)} = \frac{3}{2}.$$

So $a(2^x 3^y) < 2 \cdot \frac{3}{2} = 3$. This is the least upper bound for $a(n)$ when n takes this form. It is not achievable, but one can get values arbitrarily close to it by increasing x and y. So in fact $a(n)$ does not take a maximum value.

11. Such numbers can be written as $2^{p+2r}3^q$, which reduces this problem to the same as the one above. The maximum still does not exist, and the least upper bound is still 3.

12. Repeating the argument of problem 10, we obtain that

$$a(2^x 3^y 5^z) = \frac{2^{x+1} - 1}{2^x(2-1)} \cdot \frac{3^{y+1} - 1}{3^y(3-1)} \cdot \frac{5^{x+1} - 1}{5^x(5-1)}.$$

This too increases as x, y, z increase. The upper bound can be computed by taking the limit, which gets us $\frac{2}{1} \cdot \frac{3}{2} \cdot \frac{5}{4} = \frac{15}{4}$. This is the least upper bound; a maximum value is not actually attained.

13. This sum, which is known as the harmonic series, will increase without bound. A straightforward way to see this is to note that it is strictly greater than the series seen in problem 5 of this problem set, which can be shown by doing a comparison of corresponding terms.

14. Write the sum of the first n terms of the series as follows:

$$1 + \frac{1}{2} + \frac{1}{3} + \cdots + \frac{1}{n} = \frac{n!/1 + n!/2 + n!/3 + \cdots + n!/n}{n!}.$$

Notice that $n!/1, n!/2, n!/3, \ldots n!/n$ are n distinct divisors of $n!$, but for $n > 2$ the divisor 1 is not in this list, so at least one divisor is missing from the top. Then $a(n!)$, which can be written as the sum of the divisors of n! all divided by n!, contains all the terms in the numerator above plus additional ones, so it is strictly greater than the quantity above.

15. By problem 13, the expression $1 + \frac{1}{2} + \frac{1}{3} + \cdots + \frac{1}{n}$ increases without bound as n increases. Combined with problem 14, this shows that $a(n!)$ increases without bound as n increases. So $a(n)$ is unbounded and has no maximum value.

Problem Set 4

Opener

n	1	2	3	4	5	6	7	8	9	10	11	12
P(n)	1	1	2	2	4	2	6	4	6	4	10	4

n	13	14	15	16	17	18	19	20	21	22	23	24
P(n)	12	6	8	8	16	12	18	8	12	10	22	8

1. We notice that it appears that for prime numbers p, $P(p) = p-1$. Additionally it seems that $P(p^k) = (p-1)p^{k-1}$ for primes p and that P is multiplicative.

2. As demonstrated in problem 1 of this problem set, $P(p^k) = (p-1)p^{k-1}$ and we know that $P(n)$ is multiplicative. Noting that $210 = 2 \cdot 3 \cdot 5 \cdot 7$, we compute

$$P(210) = P(2) \cdot P(3) \cdot P(5) \cdot P(7) = 1 \cdot 2 \cdot 4 \cdot 6 = 48.$$

3. a. So far in this course we have seen several multiplicative functions. As discussed in Problem Set 1 problem 1, both $\sigma(n)$ and $\sigma_2(n)$ are multiplicative. Function $a(n)$ from Problem Set 2 is multiplicative. Function $k(n)$ from Problem Set 3 is multiplicative. In this problem set, function $P(n)$ is also multiplicative.

    b. Many simple functions turn out to be multiplicative, such as $f(x) = 1$ or $f(x) = x^n$ for any positive integer n. The $\tau(n)$ function mentioned from Problem Set 3 is multiplicative.

    c. Answers will vary. A few examples would be $f(x) = c$ for any constant c that is neither 0 nor 1, $f(x) = kx$ for any k that is neither 0 nor 1, trig functions such as $f(x) = \sin(x)$, or power functions like $f(x) = 2^x$.

4. a. A simple explanation here is to look at the number before the one Katie is talking about. That number would be a multiple of 8 *and* a multiple of 15. As seen in a previous problem, such a number would also need to be a multiple of 120, so the original number must be one more than a multiple of 120.

    b. It's not true. The number 61 is a counterexample. In general, any such number would be 1 more than a multiple of 60, not 120, since 10 and 12 have a common factor.

5. a. We compute

    $$s(15) = r(15)+r(5)+r(3)+r(1) = 15+5+3+1 = 24,$$

    $$s(20) = r(20)+r(10)+r(5)+r(4)+r(2)+r(1) = 20+10+5+4+2+1 = 42.$$

    At this point we might realize that the s function is the same as the σ function, as both are the sum of the divisors of the number. Drawing on work done in the Opener of Problem Set 1, we get that the first 10 values of $s(n)$ are $1, 3, 4, 7, 6, 12, 8, 15, 13, 18$.

    b. Yes, r is multiplicative, and s seems to be multiplicative. r is definitely multiplicative because $r(ab) = r(a) \cdot r(b)$ can be directly computed, and is true for any a and b, not just ones where a and b share no common factors.

    c. s is the σ function.

6. a. $x = 6$.
    b. $x = 3$.
    c. $x = 2, 6$.
    d. No solutions.
    e. $x = 3, 4$.
    f. $x = 1, 2, 4$.
    g. $x = 3, 5, 6$.
    h. $x = 1, 2, 3, 4, 5, 6$

Neat Stuff

7. a. We will consider each of these cases in turn.
    - Let $n = 3$. We note that both 1 and 2 have no common factors higher than 1 with 3. Since 3 clearly has a common

factor of 3 with itself, we conclude that $\phi(3) = 2$.

- Let $n = 5$. We note that 1, 2, 3, and 4 have no common factors higher than 1 with 5. Since 5 clearly has a common factor of 5 with itself, we conclude that $\phi(5) = 4$.
- Let $n = 15$. The numbers having no common factors but 1 with 15 (that are less than 15) are 1, 2, 4, 7, 8, 11, 13, and 14. Thus $\phi(15) = 8$.

b. As we compute more values of the ϕ function, we find that $\phi(n) = P(n)$!

We begin by noticing that $\phi(p) = p - 1$ for p a prime. This is due to the fact that a prime number's only factors are 1 and itself. Thus every number from 1 to $p - 1$ shares no common factor higher than 1 with p.

In fact, we can further note that $\phi(p^k) = (p - 1)p^{k-1} = p^k - p^{k-1}$. This is due to the fact that the only numbers from 1 to p^k that will share a factor with p^k are exactly the numbers with a factor of p, that is $p, 2p, 3p, \cdots, p^2, (p + 1)p, \cdots, p^{k-1}p = p^k$. There are exactly p^{k-1} such numbers, so all the remaining numbers must share no common factors aside from 1 with p^k.

8. (a) $5S = 5 + 5^2 + 5^3 + \cdots + 5^n + 5^{n+1}$.
   (b) Subtracting S from $5S$ removes almost all the terms:
   $$4S = 5^{n+1} - 1$$

   (c) Dividing our solution for part (b) by 4 would reveal the desired form of S.
   (d) Inspired by parts (a) to (c), if we let $S = 1 + x + x^2 + x^3 + \cdots + x^n$, then we can multiply the equation by x and solve for $(x-1)S$. From here we can then solve for S and obtain that the general rule is:
   $$S = \frac{x^{n+1} - 1}{x - 1}.$$

9. The child of m, which we call t, is the number of the divisors of a number. Since $m(n)$ is always 1,

$t(n)$ is just equal to the number of terms of the form $m(n)$ we have to sum, and the number of such terms is the number of divisors of n.

10. Let the child of k be called K. The first several values of $K(n)$ are $1, 4, 6, 12, 10, 24, 14, 32, 27, 40, 22, 72, \ldots$. All the values appear to be multiples of n: for example $K(10) = 40 = 4 \cdot 10$ and $K(12) = 72 = 6 \cdot 12$. That suggests looking at $\frac{K(n)}{n}$, which gives the values $1, 2, 2, 3, 2, 4, 2, 4, 3, 4, 2, 6, \ldots$, the same values as the τ function! This suggests that

$$K(n) = \tau(n) \cdot n$$

11. **a.** We want an expression with every number from 0 to 6 as a solution. That is, we want $f(x) = 0$ for $x = 0, 1, 2, 3, 4, 5, 6$. We know that if we see a factor of $(x - n)$ in an algebraic expression, this implies that n is a solution to that expression. Thus we know that

$$x(x - 1)(x - 2)(x - 3)(x - 4)(x - 5)(x - 6)$$

will have every number in mod 7 as a solution.

b. Multiplying this out yields

$$x^7 - 21x^6 + 175x^5 - 735x^4 + 1624x^3 - 1764x^2 + 720x$$

We find that the coefficients on x^2, x^3, x^4, x^5, x^6 are all multiples of 7 and thus simplify mod 7 to zero. This leaves us with

$$x^7 + 6x = x(x^6 + 6) = x(x^6 - 1).$$

Looking back at problem 6, the last equation is solved by all the elements except zero, which could have suggested this option.

Problem Set 5

1. **a.** $\phi(3) = 2, \phi(5) = 4, \phi(15) = 8$.
   b. $\phi(2) = 1, \phi(7) = 6, \phi(14) = 6$.
   c. If p is a prime, we can say $\phi(p) = p - 1$. This is due to the fact that a prime number's only factors are 1 and itself. Thus every number from 1 to $p - 1$ shares no common factor higher than 1 with p.
   d. Note that if p and q are distinct primes, then the only numbers sharing factors with pq

that are less than pq are the multiples of p
and the multiples of q. That is, the numbers
$p, 2p, 3p, \ldots, (q-1)p, qp$ and $q, 2q, \ldots, (p-1)q, pq$.

Note that with the exception of $k_1 = q, k_2 = p$, there can be no $k_1 p = k_2 q$ with $1 \leqslant k_1 \leqslant q, 1 \leqslant k_2 \leqslant p$. This is again due to the fact that a prime's only factors are 1 and itself. Thus no k_1 in the range aside from p itself has a factor of p and similarly no k_2 has a factor of q aside from q. Since these are the only numbers sharing factors greater than 1 with pq, we can count them and then subtract that value from pq. There are q multiples of p and p multiples of q, but we must subtract 1 since pq is counted twice. Thus we have

$$\phi(pq) = pq - (p + q - 1) = pq - p - q + 1.$$

Note that in fact, this factors as $(p-1)(q-1)$ so $\phi(pq) = \phi(p)\phi(q)$. $\phi(n)$ is actually in general multiplicative (we will not prove this here, but it's true)!

1. Note that in this case, $g(n)$ is exactly the function that takes the sum of the reciprocals of the divisors of n. Note that this means that $g(n) = a(n)$, the function we saw in Problem Set 2.

    a. $g(3) = \frac{4}{3}$, $g(5) = \frac{6}{5}$, $g(15) = \frac{8}{5}$.
    b. $g(2) = \frac{3}{2}$, $g(7) = \frac{8}{7}$, $g(14) = \frac{12}{7}$.
    c. For any prime p, the divisors of p are only 1 and p, so we have

$$g(p) = 1 + \frac{1}{p} = \frac{p+1}{p}.$$

Opener

n	1	2	3	4	5	6	7	8	9	10	11	12
$r(n)$	1	2	3	4	5	6	7	8	9	10	11	12

n	13	14	15	16	17	18	19	20	21	22	23	24
$r(n)$	13	14	15	16	17	18	19	20	21	22	23	24

It turns out that $r(n) = n$. One way to see this is to consider the set of fractions

$$\frac{1}{n}, \frac{2}{n}, \ldots, \frac{n}{n}.$$

Clearly there are n of these. How many are in lowest terms? Notice that if the numerator has any factor other than 1 in common with n, then the fraction is *not* in lowest terms. Thus only those with numerators relatively prime to n are in lowest terms. In particular, there are $\phi(n)$ of these.

Next, let's count how many of these fractions in lowest terms have denominator d. If d does not divide n, no fraction with denominator n can possibly reduce to a fraction with denominator d. However, if d does divide n, then we know we can reduce $\frac{d}{n}, \frac{2d}{n}, \ldots, \frac{d(n/d)}{n}$ to $\frac{1}{n/d}, \ldots, \frac{n/d}{n/d}$ respectively. But by the same logic as above, only $\phi(d)$ of these are in lowest terms! The rest reduce even more.

Thus, we see that if we add up $\phi(d)$ for all d dividing n, we end up counting all of our fractions in the set, giving us n fractions total. Since this is the definition of the child of $\phi(n)$, that tells us $r(n) = n$.

2. The child of $r(n)$ is determined by adding up $r(d)$ for all d that are divisors of n. But from above, we determined that $r(d) = d$. Thus, the child of $r(n)$ is exactly the sum of the divisors of n or $\sigma(n)$ from Problem Set 1.

3. The solutions are as follows
   (a) $x = 0, 1$.
   (b) $x = 0, 1$.
   (c) $x = 0, 1$.
   (d) $x = 0, 1, 6, 10$.
   (e) $x = 0, 1, 7, 15$.
   (f) $x = 0, 1, 15, 21$.
   (g) $x = 0, 1, 15, 21, 36, 70, 85, 91$.

Neat Stuff

4. We add 1 for each divisor of n, so the child of $m(n)$ counts the number of divisors of n. Note that this is the function $\tau(n)$ from Problem Set 3 problem 9.

5. All but functions g and m are multiplicative.

   There could be an argument here that m *is* multiplicative, but the values m computes are not in mod 12. For example, $m(5) \cdot m(7) = 35$ while $m(35) = 11$.

6. If a function is multiplicative, that means $f(ab) = f(a)f(b)$ if a and b have no common factors greater than 1. Note that this implies that $f(1) = f(1 \cdot 1) =$

$f(1)f(1)$ so $f(1) = (f(1))^2$. The only values that equal their square are 1 and 0, so $f(1)$ must be 1 or 0 if f is multiplicative.

7. The sum of two multiplicative functions is not necessarily multiplicative. In particular, if f and g are two multiplicative functions with $f(1) = g(1) = 1$, then the sum $h = f + g$ has $h(1) = 2$. As proved in the previous problem, this means h cannot be multiplicative.

    The product of two multiplicative functions *is* multiplicative. Let $h_2(n) = f(n)g(n)$. Then we see that

    $$\begin{aligned} h_2(ab) &= f(ab)g(ab) \\ &= f(a)f(b)g(a)g(b) \\ &= [f(a)g(a)][f(b)g(b)] \\ &= h_2(a)h_2(b). \end{aligned}$$

8. Yes. It can be proven by thinking about how multiplicative functions are built. A full proof follows but is not expected at this point in the course.

    Let r be a multiplicative function and s its child. We write $a \mid b$ for a divides b, and the notation $s(n) = \sum_{d\mid n} r(d)$ means that we sum $r(d)$ over all of the positive integer divisors d of n. So this equation is equivalent to s being the child of r.

    Let m, n be relatively prime. Then if d, d' are divisors of m, n respectively, they are also relatively prime. Using this observation, we find that

    $$\begin{aligned} s(m)s(n) &= \left(\sum_{d\mid m} r(d) \right) \left(\sum_{d'\mid n} r(d') \right), \\ &= \sum_{d\mid m} \sum_{d'\mid n} (r(d)r(d')), \\ &= \sum_{d\mid m} \sum_{d'\mid n} r(d \cdot d'), \\ s(mn) &= \sum_{d\mid mn} r(d). \end{aligned}$$

    Define the two sets $S_1 = \{d \cdot d' \mid d \text{ divides } m, d' \text{ divides } n\}$ and $S_2 = \{d \mid d \text{ divides } mn\}$.

    First we show $S_1 \subseteq S_2$. Let d, d' be divisors of m, n respectively; we want to show dd' divides mn. Let $m = kd, n = k'd'$; these equations come from the definition of divisibility. Then $mn = kk'dd'$, so dd' divides mn as desired.

Now we show $S_2 \subseteq S_1$. Let d be a divisor of mn. Notice that $d = \gcd(d, mn)$. Using the result from problem 6 about the function y being multiplicative, we have $\gcd(d, m) \gcd(d, n) = \gcd(d, mn) = d$. Since $\gcd(d, m), \gcd(d, n)$ are respectively divisors of m, n and d is their product, d is an element of S_1, as desired.

Therefore $S_1 = S_2$. That means the terms of the right-hand-side of the last two lines in the equations above match exactly, implying that $s(mn) = s(m)s(n)$. This completes the proof.

9. Suppose A, B are the centers of the circles they are inside, C, D are points of tangency between the circles and given line, and E, F are points of tangency between two circles. We construct G on AC with BF perpendicular to AC. Let the desired diameter be x. We are given that $AC = AE = AF = 1/2$ and $BE = BD = x/2$. Because the diagram has reflectional symmetry about line DF, we can conclude that B lies on this line and that it is perpendicular to the given line CD. Therefore AFDC is a square of side length $1/2$. Since GB is parallel to CD, we have AFGB, GBDC both rectangles. Thus $GB = CD = 1/2$ and $GC = BD = x/2$. Then $AG = AC - GC = \frac{1-x}{2}$. Furthermore $AB = AE + BE = \frac{1+x}{2}$. By the Pythagorean theorem on right triangle AGB,

$$AG^2 + GB^2 = AB^2,$$

$$\left(\frac{1-x}{2}\right)^2 + \left(\frac{1}{2}\right)^2 = \left(\frac{1+x}{2}\right)^2,$$

After expanding and simplifying the last equation, the x^2 terms cancel and we are left with $x = \frac{1}{4}$. So this is the desired diameter.

10. Suppose A, B are the centers of the large circles, C is the center of the circle of diameter $\frac{1}{4}$ and D, E, F are points of tangency between a circle and line. We construct G on AD so that BG is perpendicular to AD, and similarly we construct H on CF with BH perpendicular to CF.

Let x be the desired diameter. Note that $AD = 1/2$, $BE = x/2$, $CF = 1/8$ (from the last problem), $AB = \frac{1+x}{2}$, and $BC = \frac{1+4x}{8}$. We also note that since

AD, BE, CF are parallel, we have that GBED and BCFE are rectangles, so $GD = HF = BE = x/2$ and $GH = DF = 1/2$ (the length of DF was computed in the last problem). This gives us $AG = AD - GD = \frac{1-x}{2}$ and $CH = CF - HF = \frac{1-4x}{8}$. Let the length of $GB = y$, then $BH = \frac{1}{2} - y$. Applying the Pythagorean Theorem to right triangles AGB, CHB, we get the following system of equations:

$$\left(\frac{1-x}{2}\right)^2 + y^2 = \left(\frac{1+x}{2}\right)^2,$$

$$\left(\frac{1-4x}{8}\right)^2 + \left(\frac{1}{2} - y\right)^2 = \left(\frac{1+4x}{8}\right)^2.$$

The top one simplifies to $x = y^2$. The bottom simplifies to $\frac{x}{4} = \left(\frac{1}{2} - y\right)^2$. Therefore $\frac{y^2}{4} = \left(\frac{1}{2} - y\right)^2$. We can square root both sides since both sides are positive, giving us $\frac{y}{2} = \frac{1}{2} - y$, which can be solved getting $y = \frac{1}{3}$. Plugging into $x = y^2$ gives $x = \frac{1}{9}$, the desired diameter.

11. The rule for the child is $K_5(n) = n$ when n isn't a multiple of 5 and $K_5(n) = 2n$ when it is.

12. Suppose that there exist b, c such that $ab = ac$ (mod n). This means n divides $a(b - c)$. Since $\gcd(a, n) = 1$, this implies that n divides $b - c$, so $b = c$ (mod n). What we have just shown is that if $b \neq c$ (mod n), then $ab \neq ac$ (mod n). As a result, the n numbers $a \cdot 0, a \cdot 1, a \cdot 2, \ldots a \cdot (n-1)$ are all distinct modulo n. Yet there are only n different remainders that can be left mod n, so in fact $a \cdot 0, a \cdot 1, a \cdot 2, \ldots a \cdot (n-1)$ must be $0, 1, 2, \ldots n-1$ in some order, which is exactly what we wanted to show.

13. (a) $x = 1, 2$.
    (b) $x = 1, 2, 3, 4$.
    (c) $x = 1, 2, 3, 4, 5, 6$.
    (d) $x = 1, 2, 3, 4, 5, 6, 7, 8, 9, 10$.
    (e) $x = 1$.

14. The different values of x that satisfy $x^2 = 1 \bmod p$ are $x = 1$ and $x = p - 1$.

15. (a) $x = 1, 2, 4$.
    (b) $x = 1, 3, 4, 9, 10, 12$.
    (c) $x = 1, 2, 4, 8, 9, 13, 15, 16$.
    (d) $x = 1, 4, 5, 6, 7, 9, 11, 16, 17$.

16. (a) $x = 1, 2, 4$.

(b) $x = 3, 5, 6$.

(c) $x = 1, 3, 4, 9, 10, 12$.

(d) $x = 1, 2, 4, 8, 9, 13, 15, 16$.

(e) $x = 1, 4, 5, 6, 7, 9, 11, 16, 17$.

17. A useful way to think about this problem will be to break 165 down into relatively prime factors that are as small as possible. We know $165 = 3 \cdot 5 \cdot 11$. We know that any solution in mod 165 must also be a solution in mods 3, 5, and 11.

- $x^2 - 4x + 3 = (x - 1)(x - 3) = 0$ in mod 3 implies $x = 0, 1$.
- $x^2 - 4x + 3 = (x - 1)(x - 3) = 0$ in mod 5 implies $x = 1, 3$.
- $x^2 - 4x + 3 = (x - 1)(x - 3) = 0$ in mod 11 implies $x = 1, 3$.

Since 3, 5, and 11 share no common factors, a solution satisfies $x^2 - 4x + 3 = 0$ in mods 3, 5, and 11 if and only if it is a solution in mod $3 \cdot 5 \cdot 11 = 165$. Determining every possible combination gives us $x = 1, 3, 36, 58, 78, 91, 111, 133$ as our solutions.

18. Let m and n be relatively prime integers. Then $c(mn)$ is the number of solutions to the equation $x^2 = 1$ in mod mn. Note that if x is a solution in mod mn, it clearly must be a solution in both mod m and mod n. Likewise, since m and n share no common factors, a solution satisfies $x^2 = 1$ in mods m and n if and only if it is a solution in mod mn. Thus, $c(mn) = c(m)c(n)$ and c is multiplicative.

Problem Set 6

Opener

n	1	2	3	4	5	6	7	8	9	10	11	12
$m(n)$	1	1	1	1	1	1	1	1	1	1	1	1
$t(n)$	1	2	2	3	2	4	2	4	3	4	2	6
$u(n)$	1	3	3	6	3	9	3	10	6	9	3	18

n	13	14	15	16	17	18	19	20	21	22	23	24
$m(n)$	1	1	1	1	1	1	1	1	1	1	1	1
$t(n)$	2	4	4	5	2	6	2	6	4	4	2	8
$u(n)$	3	9	9	15	3	18	3	18	9	9	3	30

1. All three of these functions are multiplicative! Note that $m(n) = 1$ for any n, so for any a and b, $f(ab) = f(a)f(b) = 1 \cdot 1 = 1$.

2. The table below shows the values filled in. An extra row for a general prime power is also shown to demonstrate the pattern.

n	$m(n)$	$t(n)$	$u(n)$
1	1	1	1
p	1	2	3
p^2	1	3	6
p^3	1	4	10
p^4	1	5	15
p^k	1	$k+1$	$\frac{(k+1)(k+2)}{2}$

3. By definition, $m(n) = 1$ for any integer n. Therefore $m(420) = 1$. From the table, you may have noticed that $t(n)$ simply returns the number of factors n has. Therefore $t(420) = 24$. Since u is multiplicative, you can find $u(420)$ by taking the product of values for the relatively prime factors of 420:

$$u(420) = u(4) \cdot u(3) \cdot u(5) \cdot u(7) = 6 \cdot 3 \cdot 3 \cdot 3 = 162.$$

4. (a) If n is one more than a multiple of 3 and one more than a multiple of 8, then the most you can say about n is that it is one more than a multiple of $3 \times 8 = 24$. From what we know about n, we have that $n = 3a + 1 = 8b + 1$ for some positive integers a and b. The second equality implies that a is divisible by 8 and hence we can express $a = 8c$ for some positive integer c. Therefore we have that $n = 24c + 1$, and thus n is one more than a multiple of 24.

   (b) Similarly if n is two more than a multiple of 3 and seven more than a multiple of 8, then the most one can say about n is that it is 23 more – or one less – than a multiple of $3 \times 8 = 24$. From what we know we about n, we have that $n = 3a + 2 = 8b + 7$ for some positive integers a and b. However, we can rewrite these equalities as $n = 3a' - 1 = 8b' - 1$ for $a' = a + 1$ and $b' = b + 1$. By a similar logic from Part A, we then have that a' is divisible by 8 and thus $n = 24c - 1$ for some positive integer c. Hence, n is one less or 23 more than a multiple of 24.

5. It turns out this happens quite often:

   $n = 1, 5, 7, 11, 13, 17, 19, 23, 25, 29, 31, 35, 37, 41, 43, 47.$

6. (a) The solutions are $x = \pm 1$ or rather $x = 1$ and $x = 2$.
   (b) The solutions are $x = 1, 3, 5, 7$.
   (c) The solutions are the first 8 solutions from problem 5: $x = 1, 5, 7, 11, 13, 17, 19, 23$.
   (d) The solutions are $x = 1, 17, 19, 35, 37, 53, 55, 71$. Note that each solution must also be a solution in mod 24.

7. (a) The number that contribute to $\phi(1)$ is 1. Similarly for $\phi(3)$, we have $1, 2$. Again for $\phi(7)$ we have $1, 2, 3, 4, 5, 6$. And finally for $\phi(21)$, we have $1, 2, 4, 5, 8, 10, 11, 13, 16, 17, 19, 20$.
   (b) From counting the numbers above, we find that the sum

   $$\phi(1) + \phi(3) + \phi(7) + \phi(21) = 21.$$

   (c) We begin by expanding the multiplication:

   $$1+(p-1)+(q-1)+(p-1)(q-1) = 1+(p-1)+(q-1)+(pq-p-q+1).$$

   Combining like terms, we arrive at

   $$1 + (p-1) + (q-1) + (p-1)(q-1) = pq.$$

Neat Stuff

8. The table below shows the values filled in. An extra row for a general prime power is also shown to demonstrate the pattern.

n	$\sigma(n)$	$a(n)$	$\phi(n)$
1	1	1	1
p	$p+1$	$\frac{p+1}{p}$	$p-1$
p^2	p^2+p+1	$\frac{p^2+p+1}{p^2}$	$p(p-1)$
p^3	p^3+p^2+p+1	$\frac{p^3+p^2+p+1}{p^3}$	$p^2(p-1)$
p^4	$p^4+p^3+p^2+p+1$	$\frac{p^4+p^3+p^2+p+1}{p^4}$	$p^3(p-1)$
p^k	$\sum_{i=0}^{k} p^i$	$\frac{\sum_{i=0}^{k} p^i}{p^k}$	$p^{k-1}(p-1)$

Note that an equivalent form for the summations in the last line $\sum_{i=0}^{k} p^i = \frac{p^{k+1}-1}{p-1}$. Additionally, an alternate way to express the sums of the middle column is the $\sum_{i=-k}^{0} p^i$; for instance,

$$\frac{p^2+p+1}{p^2} = 1 + p^{-1} + p^{-2} = 1 + \frac{1}{p} + \frac{1}{p^2}.$$

9. The first several entries of the column would be
1, 4, 10, 20, 35. In general $v(p^k) = \frac{(k+1)(k+2)(k+3)}{6}$.
Using this we can compute $v(420) = v(4)v(3)v(5)v(7) = 10 \cdot 4^3 = 640$.

10. We first note that 3, 5, and 7 share no common factors greater than 1.

   a. Since x is 0 mod 5 and 0 mod 7, we know that $x = 35a$ for some integer a. Additionally, we know x is 1 mod 3, so we know $x = 3b + 1$ for some integer b. Thus we want to find a multiple of 35 that is one more than a multiple of 3, and this will be our x. We only need to check multiples up to 105 since we are looking for an answer mod 105. We find that $x = 70 = 3(23) + 1$ in mod 105.

   b. Since y is 0 mod 3 and 0 mod 7, we know that $y = 21a$ for some integer a. Additionally, we know y is 1 mod 5, so we know $y = 5b + 1$ for some integer b. Thus we want to find a multiple of 21 that is one more than a multiple of 5, and this will be our y. We only need to check multiples up to 105 since we are looking for an answer mod 105. We find that $y = 21 = 5(4) + 1$ in mod 105.

   c. Since z is 0 mod 3 and 0 mod 5, we know that $z = 15a$ for some integer a. Additionally, we know z is 1 mod 7, so we know $z = 7b + 1$ for some integer b. Thus we want to find a multiple of 15 that is one more than a multiple of 7, and this will be our z. We only need to check multiples up to 105 since we are looking for an answer mod 105. We find that $z = 15 = 7(2) + 1$ in mod 105.

   d. We can calculate

   $$2x + 3y + 4z = 2(70) + 3(21) + 4(15) = 263$$

   which in mod 105 is 53.

11. Let's use the work in problem 10 of this problem set to help us solve this problem. Note that we have already determined values mod 105 that are 0 mod two of our modulae and 1 mod the last. Thus if we wish to find a number mod 105 that is a in mod 3, b in mod 5, and c in mod 7, we can simply take
   $$ax + by + cz$$

where x, y, z are as determined in problem 10 parts a to c. This makes sense since ax will be a mod 3, but 0 mod 5 and 0 mod 7. Similar logic holds for by and cz. Thus, we can find a value that is 2 mod 3, 3 mod 5, and 4 mod 7 in mod 105 by computing

$$2x + 3y + 4z = 2(70) + 3(21) + 4(15) = 263$$

and taking our result mod 105, yielding 53. As a sanity check, we note that

$$53 = 3(17) + 2 = 5(10) + 3 = 7(7) + 4$$

so this result does meet our criteria.

12. (a) If $x^2 = 1 \bmod 3$, then $x = 1, 2$.
    (b) If $x^2 = 1 \bmod 5$, then $x = 1, 4$.
    (c) If $x^2 = 1 \bmod 7$, then $x = 1, 6$.
    (d) If $x^2 = 1 \bmod 15$, then $x = 1, 4, 11, 14$.
    (e) If $x^2 = 1 \bmod 21$, then $x = 1, 8, 13, 20$.
    (f) If $x^2 = 1 \bmod 35$, then $x = 1, 6, 29, 34$.
    (g) If $x^2 = 1 \bmod 105$, then $x = 1, 29, 34, 41, 64, 71, 76, 104$.
    (h) If $x^2 = 1 \bmod 420$, then

    $$x = 1, 29, 41, 71, 139, 169, 181, 209, 211, 239, 251, 281, 349, 379, 391, 419.$$

13. (a) If $x^2 = 2 \bmod 3$, then there are no solutions.
    (b) If $x^2 = 2 \bmod 7$, then $x = 3, 4$.
    (c) If $x^2 = 2 \bmod 17$, then $x = 6, 11$.
    (d) If $x^2 = 2 \bmod 21$, then there are no solutions.
    (e) If $x^2 = 2 \bmod 51$, then there are no solutions.
    (f) If $x^2 = 2 \bmod 119$, then $x = 11, 45, 74, 108$. Note that $119 = 7 \cdot 17$.
    (g) If $x^2 = 1 \bmod 105$, then there are no solutions.

Problem Set 7

Opener

For convenience we will **bold** numbers that are solutions in mod 5, and *italicize* numbers that are solutions in mod 12.

Any x that is 0 or 2 in mod 5 is a solution to $x^2 = 2x$ in mod 5. Any x that is 0, 2, 6, or 8 in mod 12 is a solution to $x^2 = 2x$ in mod 12.

0	1	2	3	4	**5**	*6*	7	*8*	9	**10**	11
12	13	*14*	**15**	16	**17**	*18*	19	*20*	21	**22**	23
24	**25**	26	27	28	29	**30**	31	*32*	33	34	**35**
36	**37**	*38*	39	**40**	41	*42*	43	*44*	**45**	46	**47**
48	49	*50*	51	**52**	53	*54*	**55**	*56*	**57**	58	59

In particular this means 0, 2, 12, 20, 30, 32, 42, and 50 are the solutions to $x^2 = 2x$ in mod 60.

We see that $f(5) = 2$, $f(12) = 4$, and $f(60) = 8$...it appears that this function might be multiplicative!

1. First we will find in mod 60 a number x that is 1 mod 5 and 0 mod 12 and a number y that is 0 mod 5 and 1 mod 12. By a bit of trial and error, we can fairly quickly determine that $x = 36$ and $y = 25$ in mod 60. Now we know that the number we want can be calculated by

$$3x + 7y = 3(36) + 7(25) = 283.$$

We note that this is 43 in mod 60. Any number that is 43 in mod 60 will satisfy these conditions.

2. a. We note that because 5 is prime, every number less than 5 is relatively prime to 5. Thus, $\phi(5) = 4$.
   The numbers 1, 5, 7, and 11 are relatively prime to 12, so $\phi(12) = 4$.
   b. If a number shares no common factors with 5 and no common factors with 12, it cannot share any common factors with 60.
   c. We will **bold** any number relatively prime to 5 in mod 5 and *italicize* any number relatively prime to 12. Any number that is both ***bold and italicized*** is relatively prime to 60.

1	2	3	4	*5*	6	*7*	8	9	10	*11*	12
13	14	15	16	***17***	18	***19***	20	**21**	22	**23**	24
25	26	27	28	**29**	30	***31***	32	33	34	*35*	36
37	38	39	40	***41***	42	***43***	44	45	46	***47***	48
49	50	**51**	52	**53**	54	*55*	56	**57**	58	***59***	60

   Thus the numbers relatively prime to 60 are 1, 7, 11, 13, 17, 19, 23, 29, 31, 37, 41, 43, 47, 49, 53, and 59.
   d. Counting the numbers relatively prime to 60 that we found above, we see $\phi(60) = 16$, which is consistent with the behavior of a multiplicative function.

3. Find the solutions in mod 5 and mod 12 first: there are 4 of each, and they are the same solutions as the numbers that share no common factors with 5 or 12. It makes sense that the same work will help find solutions in mod 60, and it does.

Then $P(5) = 4, P(12) = 4, P(60) = 16$. It appears $P(n)$ behaves exactly like $\phi(n)$.

4. From the overlaid grid on the handout, we have that the first small circle has a diameter of $1/4$ centered at $(1/2, 1/8)$; while the second small circle has a diameter of $1/9$ centered at $(1/3, 1/18)$.

5.

+	1	2	3	4	5	6
1	2	3	4	5	6	7
2	3	4	5	6	7	8
3	4	5	6	7	8	9
4	5	6	7	8	9	10
5	6	7	8	9	10	11
6	7	8	9	10	11	12

$\times$	x	x^2	x^3	x^4	x^5	x^6
x	x^2	x^3	x^4	x^5	x^6	x^7
x^2	x^3	x^4	x^5	x^6	x^7	x^8
x^3	x^4	x^5	x^6	x^7	x^8	x^9
x^4	x^5	x^6	x^7	x^8	x^9	x^{10}
x^5	x^6	x^7	x^8	x^9	x^{10}	x^{11}
x^6	x^7	x^8	x^9	x^{10}	x^{11}	x^{12}

For cell (i, j) in the left table, the sum $i + j$ equals the exponent on x in the cell (i, j) on the right. This makes sense since $x^i \cdot x^j = x^{i+j}$. Note also that this means that the number of ways to roll a particular sum n is the coefficient on x^n in the expansion of $(x + x^2 + x^3 + x^4 + x^5 + x^6)^2$.

6. The easiest way to determine the number of ways to roll a sum n with four dice is to expand $(x + x^2 + x^3 + x^4 + x^5 + x^6)^4$ and examine the coefficient on x^n in the resulting polynomial. The expansion of this polynomial yields

$$(x + x^2 + x^3 + x^4 + x^5 + x^6)^4 = x^{24} + 4x^{23} + 10x^{22} + 20x^{21} + 35x^{20} + 56x^{19} + 80x^{18} + 104x^{17} + 125x^{16} + 140x^{15} + 146x^{14} + 140x^{13} + 125x^{12} + 104x^{11} + 80x^{10} + 56x^9 + 35x^8 + 20x^7 + 10x^6 + 4x^5 + x^4.$$

Putting this data into histogram form gives us:

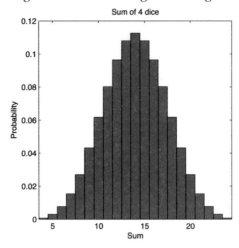

Neat Stuff

7. (a) The first 36 values of $c(n)$ are filled in the table below.

n	+1	+2	+3	+4	+5	+6
0	1	1/2	2/3	1/2	4/5	1/3
6	6/7	1/2	2/3	2/5	10/11	1/3
12	12/13	3/7	8/15	1/2	16/17	1/3
18	18/19	2/5	4/7	5/11	22/23	1/3
24	4/5	6/13	2/3	3/7	28/29	4/15
30	30/31	1/2	20/33	8/17	24/35	1/3

(b) The table below shows the values filled in. An extra row for a general prime power is also shown to demonstrate the rather obvious pattern.

n	$c(n)$
1	1
p	$1 - \frac{1}{p}$
p^2	$1 - \frac{1}{p}$
p^3	$1 - \frac{1}{p}$
p^4	$1 - \frac{1}{p}$
p^k	$1 - \frac{1}{p}$

(c) It is possible, but not with prime powers. A number with $c(n) < 0.1$ needs a large number of distinct prime factors.

8. (a) The first 36 values of $d(n)$ are filled in the table below.

n	+1	+2	+3	+4	+5	+6
0	1.0000	0.7500	0.8889	0.8750	0.9600	0.6667
6	0.9796	0.9375	0.9630	0.7200	0.9917	0.7778
12	0.9941	0.7347	0.8533	0.9688	0.9965	0.7222
18	0.9972	0.8400	0.8707	0.7438	0.9981	0.8333
24	0.9920	0.7456	0.9877	0.8571	0.9988	0.6400
30	0.9990	0.9844	0.8815	0.7474	0.9404	0.8426

(b) Since d is the product of two multiplicative functions, it must be multiplicative.

(c) The maximum value of d is 1. It's unclear at this point where d has a minimum, or what it is.

9. (a) The only solution is $x = 1$ since $1^2 + 1 = 2$ in mod 3 and no other values work.

(b) The solutions are $x = 1$ and $x = 3$ in mod 5.

(c) The solutions are $x = 1$ and $x = 5$ in mod 7. Factoring $x^2 + x - 2 = (x+2)(x-1)$ could help avoid testing many values for larger primes.

(d) A particular x value must be a solution in both mod 3 and mod 5 to be a solution in mod 15. We will use the method of the Opener, **bolding** solutions in mod 3 and *italicizing* solutions in mod 5. A number that is both ***bolded and italicized*** is a solution in mod 15.

0	*1*	2	**3**	4
5	**6**	7	8	9
10	***11***	12	***13***	14

Thus, our solutions to $x^2 + x = 2$ in mod 15 are 1 and 13.

(e) We know the prime factorization of 21 is $21 = 3 \cdot 7$. Thus in order to be a solution in mod 21, a particular x value must be a solution in both mod 3 and mod 7. In fact, since 3 and 7 share no common factors, a solution satisfies $x^2 + x = 2$ in both mods 3 and 7 if and only if it is a solution in mod $3 \cdot 7 = 21$. We will use the method of the Opener, **bolding** solutions in mod 3 and *italicizing* solutions in mod 7. A number that is both ***bolded and italicized*** is a solution in mod 21.

0	*1*	2	**3**	4	*5*	6
7	*8*	9	**10**	11	*12*	**13**
14	**15**	*16*	17	18	***19***	20

Thus, our solutions to $x^2 + x = 2$ in mod 21 are 1 and 19.

(f) We know the prime factorization of 35 is $35 = 5 \cdot 7$. Thus in order to be a solution in mod 25, a particular x value must be a solution in both mod 5 and mod 7. In fact, since 5 and 7 share no common factors, a solution satisfies $x^2 + x = 2$ in both mods 5 and 7 if and only if it is a solution in mod $5 \cdot 7 = 35$. We will use the method of the Opener, **bolding** solutions in mod 5 and *italicizing* solutions in mod 7. A number that is both ***bolded and italicized*** is a solution in mod 35.

0	*1*	2	**3**	4	*5*	**6**
7	***8***	9	10	**11**	*12*	**13**
14	*15*	**16**	17	**18**	*19*	20
21	*22*	**23**	24	25	***26***	27
28	*29*	30	**31**	32	***33***	34

Thus, our solutions to $x^2 + x = 2$ in mod 35 are 1, 8, 26, and 33.

(g) We know the prime factorization of 105 is $105 = 3 \cdot 5 \cdot 7$. Thus in order to be a solution in mod 105, a particular x value must be a solution in mod 3, mod 5, and mod 7. In fact, since 7 and 15 share no common factors, a solution satisfies $x^2 + x = 2$ in both mods 7 and 15 if and only if it is a solution in mod $7 \cdot 15 = 105$. We will use the method of the Opener, **bolding** solutions in mod 7 and *italicizing* solutions in mod 15. A number that is both ***bolded and italicized*** is a solution in mod 105.

0	*1*	2	3	4	**5**	6	7	**8**	9	10	11	**12**	*13*	14
15	*16*	17	18	**19**	20	21	**22**	23	24	25	**26**	27	*28*	**29**
30	*31*	32	**33**	34	35	**36**	37	38	39	**40**	41	42	**43**	44
45	*46*	**47**	48	49	**50**	51	52	53	**54**	55	56	**57**	*58*	59
60	**61**	62	63	**64**	65	66	67	**68**	69	70	**71**	72	*73*	74
75	*76*	77	**78**	79	80	81	**82**	83	84	**85**	86	87	*88*	**89**
90	*91*	**92**	93	94	95	**96**	97	98	**99**	100	101	102	*103*	104

Thus, our solutions to $x^2 + x = 2$ in mod 105 are 1, 43, 61, and 103.

10. We will use the same method we have used to solve similar problems. We first note that 3, 5, and 11 share no common factors greater than 1.

a. Since x is 0 mod 5 and 0 mod 11, we know that $x = 55a$ for some integer a. Additionally, we know x is 1 mod 3, so we know $x = 3b + 1$ for some integer b. Thus we want to find a multiple of 55 that is one more than a multiple of 3, and this will be our x. We only need to check multiples up to 165 since we are looking for an answer mod 165. We find that $x = 55 = 3(38) + 1$ in mod 165.

b. Since y is 0 mod 3 and 0 mod 11, we know that $y = 33a$ for some integer a. Additionally, we know y is 1 mod 5, so we know $y = 5b + 1$ for some integer b. Thus we want to find a multiple of 33 that is one more than a multiple of 5, and this will be our y. We only need to check multiples up to 165 since we are looking for an answer mod 165. We find that $y = 66 = 5(13) + 1$ in mod 165.

c. Since z is 0 mod 3 and 0 mod 5, we know that $z = 15a$ for some integer a. Additionally, we know z is 1 mod 11, so we know $z = 11b + 1$ for some integer b. Thus we want to find a multiple of 15 that is one more than a multiple of 11, and this will be our z. We only need to check multiples up to 165 since we are looking for an answer mod 165. We find that $z = 45 = 11(4) + 1$ in mod 165.

d. We can calculate

$$2x + 4y + 8z = 2(55) + 4(66) + 8(45) = 734$$

which in mod 165 is 74.

11. Take advantage of the work in problem 10 of this problem set to help us solve this problem. Note that we have already determined values mod 165 that are 0 mod two of our modulae and 1 mod the last. Thus if we wish to find a number mod 165 that is a in mod 3, b in mod 5, and c in mod 11, we can simply take

$$ax + by + cz$$

where x, y, z are as determined in problem 10 parts a to c. This makes sense since ax will be a mod 3, but 0 mod 5 and 0 mod 7. Similar logic holds for by and cz. Thus, we can find a value that is 2 mod 3, 4 mod 5, and 8 mod 11 in mod 165 by computing

$$2x + 4y + 8z = 2(55) + 4(66) + 8(45) = 734$$

and taking our result mod 165, yielding 74. As a sanity check, we note that

$$74 = 3(24) + 2 = 5(14) + 4 = 11(6) + 8$$

so this result does meet our criteria.

12. We know that $165 = 3 \cdot 5 \cdot 11$. We can begin by taking advantage of work from a previous Set, namely Set 6 problem 12. In this problem, we determined the solutions to $x^2 = 1$ in mod 3 are $x = 1$ and $x = 2$. We also found that the solutions to $x^2 = 1$ in mod 5 are $x = 1$ and $x = 4$. Next we will determine solutions for mod 11. We can accomplish this by simply plugging in all possible values mod 11, which results in the discovery that x must be 1 or 10 to satisfy $x^2 = 1$.

In our Opener for this problem set as well as in problems in past sets such as Problem Set 6 problems 12 and 13, we have seen that the number of solutions to equations in mod n (call this value $f(n)$) seems to be a multiplicative function. If this is true, we would expect the number of solutions in mod 165 to be

$$f(165) = f(3) \cdot f(5) \cdot f(11) = 2 \cdot 2 \cdot 2 = 8.$$

We can confirm this by using the method from the Opener this problem set to determine the actual solutions. We will **bold** numbers that are solutions to $x^2 = 1$ in mod 15 (we found these in Set 6 number 12) and *italicize* solutions in mod 11. Number that are both ***bolded and italicized*** are solutions in mod 165.

0	*1*	2	3	**4**	5	6	7	8	9	*10*	**11**	12	13	**14**
15	**16**	17	18	**19**	20	21	22	23	24	25	**26**	27	28	**29**
30	**31**	32	33	***34***	35	36	37	38	39	40	**41**	42	*43*	**44**
45	**46**	47	48	**49**	50	51	52	53	*54*	55	***56***	57	58	**59**
60	**61**	62	63	**64**	*65*	66	*67*	68	69	70	**71**	72	73	**74**
75	***76***	77	*78*	**79**	80	81	82	83	84	85	**86**	*87*	88	***89***
90	**91**	92	93	**94**	95	96	97	*98*	99	*100*	**101**	102	103	**104**
105	**106**	107	108	***109***	110	*111*	112	113	114	115	**116**	117	118	**119**
120	**121**	*122*	123	**124**	125	126	127	128	129	130	***131***	132	*133*	**134**
135	**136**	137	138	**139**	140	141	*142*	143	*144*	145	**146**	147	148	**149**
150	**151**	152	*153*	**154**	*155*	156	157	158	159	160	**161**	162	163	***164***

Thus our solutions in mod 165 are 1, 34, 56, 76, 89, 109, 131, and 164. So, as expected, we have 8 solutions to $x^2 = 1$ in mod 165.

13. **a.** Let a, c be two numbers with no common factors. Then

$$b(ac) = \frac{1}{ac} = \frac{1}{a} \cdot \frac{1}{c} = b(a) \cdot b(c)$$

so b is a multiplicative function.

b. This is the σ_2 function we explored in Problem Set 1. It is, in fact, a multiplicative function.

c. Let a, b be two numbers that share no common factors. Let's break this up into cases:

- $a = 4k_1 + 1$, $b = 4k_2 + 1$ for some positive integers k_1, k_2.
  Then we know that

  $$ab = (4k_1 + 1)(4k_2 + 1)$$
  $$= 16k_1 k_2 + 4k_1 + 4k_2 + 1$$
  $$= 4(4k_1 k_2 + k_1 + k_2) + 1.$$

  So $\chi(ab) = 1 = 1 \cdot 1 = \chi(a) \cdot \chi(b)$.

- $a = 4k_1 + 1$, $b = 4k_2 - 1$ for some positive integers k_1, k_2. Note that this case is equivalent to if $a = 4k_1 - 1$ and $b = 4k_2 + 1$.
  Then we know that

  $$ab = (4k_1 + 1)(4k_2 - 1)$$
  $$= 16k_1 k_2 - 4k_1 + 4k_2 - 1$$
  $$= 4(4k_1 k_2 - k_1 + k_2) - 1.$$

  So $\chi(ab) = -1 = 1 \cdot -1 = \chi(a) \cdot \chi(b)$.

- $a = 4k_1 - 1$, $b = 4k_2 - 1$ for some positive integers k_1, k_2.
  Then we know that

  $$ab = (4k_1 - 1)(4k_2 - 1)$$
  $$= 16k_1 k_2 - 4k_1 - 4k_2 + 1$$
  $$= 4(4k_1 k_2 - k_1 - k_2) + 1.$$

  So $\chi(ab) = 1 = -1 \cdot -1 = \chi(a) \cdot \chi(b)$.

- Finally, if one of a and b is even, we know the product ab must be even, so $\chi(ab) = 0 = \chi(a) \cdot \chi(b)$.

Thus, since this exhaustively covers all possible cases, we can conclude χ is multiplicative.

14.   **a.** This function counts the number of divisors of n, and is usually called $\tau(n)$.

   b. No matter the prime factorization of n, this function will evaluate to a product of ones. Thus, this is the function $f(n) = 1$.

   c. For any n, this function will return exactly product of the prime powers in the prime factorization is n, that is, it will simply return n itself. Here $f(n) = n$.

   d. For any prime power, f returns the sum of the divisors of that prime power. Thus for any arbitrary n, f gives the sum of the divisors, usually called $\sigma(n)$.

15.   We will do this via a counting argument. For each divisor d of n, let S_d be the subset of $\{1, 2, \ldots n\}$ such that for each $k \in S_d$ we have $\gcd(n, k) = d$. Let T_d be all integers that are at most n/d and relatively prime to n/d, which has size $\phi(n/d)$.

   We claim that for each d, if we multiply each element of T_d by d then we get S_d. If $k \in S_d$, then $\gcd(k, n) = d$, which means that $\gcd(k/d, n/d) = 1$, so $k/d \in T_d$ as desired. On the other hand if $k \in T_d$, then $\gcd(k, n/d) = 1$, so $\gcd(dk, n) = d$ as desired.

   This shows that $|S_d| = |T_d| = \phi(n/d)$. Furthermore each integer from 1 to n is in exactly one S_d, so if we sum over all the set cardinalities $|S_d|$ we get n. That is, $\sum_{d|n} |S_d| = n$, or $\sum_{d|n} \phi(n/d) = n$. This is the same as $\sum_{d|n} \phi(d) = n$ since we can replace d with n/d without changing the terms of the sum, so the proof is complete.

Problem Set 8

Opener

For convenience we will **bold** numbers satisfying $x^3 - 1 = 0$ in mod 7 and *italicize* numbers satisfying $x^3 - 1 = 0$ in mod 9. Notice that because 7 and 9 share no factors in common greater than 1, any number that satisfies both the above conditions will be a solution in mod 63. That is, any number that is both **bold *and* italicized** is a solution to $x^3 - 1 = 0$ in mod 63.

The solutions to $x^3 - 1 = 0$ in mod 7 are 1, 2, and 4 (we can simply plug in the numbers 0 to 6 to determine this). The solutions to $x^3 - 1 = 0$ in mod 9 are 1, 4, and 7. Based on earlier work, expect 9 solutions in mod 63, and this is what happens:

0	1	2	3	4	5	6	7	8
9	10	11	12	13	14	15	16	17
18	19	20	21	22	23	24	25	26
27	28	29	30	31	32	33	34	35
36	37	38	39	40	41	42	43	44
45	46	47	48	49	50	51	52	53
54	55	56	57	58	59	60	61	62

The nine solutions to $x^3 - 1 = 0$ in mod 63 are 1, 4, 16, 22, 25, 37, 43, 46, and 58.

If we let $f(n)$ be the number of solutions to our equation in mod n, we can see $f(7) = 3$, $f(9) = 3$, and $f(63) = 9$. Perhaps $f(n)$ is multiplicative!

1.   a. Consider a multiple of 63, 63x where x is an integer. We could rewrite this as 7(9x) or 9(7x), so any multiple of 63 is required to be a multiple of 7 and a multiple of 9.

     b. If our number is a multiple of 7, we know we can write it as 7x for some integer x. We also know this number is a multiple of 9. Since 7 is not divisible by 7, it must be the case that x = 9y for some integer y for 9 to divide 7x. Note that this means we can rewrite our number 7(9y) = 63y, so if a number is a multiple of both 7 and 9, it must also be a multiple of 63.

2.   a. Consider a multiple of 60, 60x where x is an integer. We could rewrite this as 6(10x) or 10(6x), so any multiple of 60 is required to be a multiple of 6 and a multiple of 10.

     b. Consider the number 30. We know that 30 is a multiple of both 6 and 10, but it is clearly not a multiple of 60. So it is not necessarily the case that just because a number is a multiple of 6 and a multiple of 10, it is also a multiple of 60. The distinction here from problem 1b of this problem set is that while 7 and 9 are relatively prime, 6 and 10 are not (they share a common factor of 2).

3. See the solution to Problem Set 7 problem 4.

4. (a) Plugging these two values into the equation, we get $2(2+c^2) = (2+c)^2$, which simplifies to $c^2 - 4c = 0$. This quadratic has roots $c = 0, 4$.

   (b) For a small circle, the value of c must be greater than 1, so the usable solution is $c = 4$, and the diameter of $\frac{1}{4}$.

   (c) Plugging these two values into the equation, we get $2(17 + c^2) = (5 + c)^2$, which simplifies to $c^2 - 10c + 9 = 0$. This quadratic has roots $c = 1, 9$.

   (d) Since the diameter of the circle we're looking for is smaller than $\frac{1}{4}$, we choose the root $c = 9$, getting a diameter of $\frac{1}{9}$.

   (e) Plugging in $a = 1, b = 9$ will get the diameter of the next small circle. The equation becomes $2(82 + c^2) = (10 + c^2)$, which simplifies to $c^2 - 20c + 64 = 0$. This quadratic has roots $c = 4, 16$. Since the diameter of the circle we're looking for is smaller than $\frac{1}{9}$, we choose the root $c = 16$, getting a diameter of $\frac{1}{16}$.

   (f) Plugging in $a = 1, b = 16$ gets $2(257 + c^2) = (17+c)^2$, which simplifies to $c^2 - 34c + 225 = 0$ with roots $c = 9, 25$. We choose the root $c = 25$ getting the diameter $\frac{1}{25}$.

5. Please reference Problem Set 7 problems 5 and 6 for solutions.

6. Let's pretend we color each instance of rock so that they are different. Let's call them RockR, RockG, and RockB (red, green, and blue) to distinguish them. Now let's count how many different orders we could play in.

   There are 5 possibilities for what is played first (Paper, RockR, RockG, RockB, or Scissors). With this decided, there are then only 4 possibilities for what is played next, then 3 for the third play, 2 for the fourth play, and the final play must be whatever is leftover. So there are $5 \cdot 4 \cdot 3 \cdot 2 \cdot 1$ ways for this to be played.

   However, in actuality different instances of Rock are not distinguishable. That is, the play Paper-RockR-RockG-RockB-Scissors is actually identical to Paper-RockG-RockB-RockR-Scissors. So now we want to find out how many times we have counted each actual play. All plays with Rocks in the same 3 slots are identical, so we really just want to know how many ways we can arrange

RockG, RockB, and RockR. By similar logic to above, we have 3 options for which is in the first slot, 2 possibilities for the second slot, then the final slot is filled with the remaining rock. So each actual play is counted $3 \cdot 2 \cdot 1$ times.

Putting this all together, the number of different ways paper could be played once, rock could be played three times, and scissors could be played once is $\dfrac{5 \cdot 4 \cdot 3 \cdot 2 \cdot 1}{3 \cdot 2 \cdot 1} = 5 \cdot 4 = 20$.

7. The expansion of $(p + r + s)^5$ is
$p^5 + 5p^4r + 5p^4s + 10p^3r^2 + 20p^3rs + 10p^3s^2 + 10p^2r^3 + 30p^2r^2s + 30p^2rs^2 + 10p^2s^3 + 5pr^4 + 20pr^3s + 30pr^2s^2 + 20prs^3 + 5ps^4 + r^5 + 5r^4s + 10r^3s^2 + 10r^2s^3 + 5rs^4 + s^5$. We are interested in the scenario with one paper, three rocks, and one scissors, so we check the coefficient of pr^3s to determine the number of ways this is possible. The coefficient of pr^3s in the polynomial above is 20, which matches the answer given in problem 6.

Neat Stuff

8. a. The multiples of 9 mod 63 are 0, 9, 18, 27, 36, 45, and 54. The only one of these that is 1 in mod 7 is 36, so $x = 36$.

    b. By similar logic to part a, we can determine $y = 28$.

    c. Evaluating the quantities yields

$x + y = 1$	$2x + y = 37$	$4x + y = 46$
$x + 4y = 22$	$2x + 4y = 58$	$4x + 4y = 4$
$x + 7y = 43$	$2x + 7y = 16$	$4x + 7y = 25$

    These quantities are identical to the solutions we determined in the Opener. That is, these are the nine solutions to $x^3 - 1 = 0$ in mod 63. We can also see that the coefficients on x are 1, 2, and 4 which we determined were the solutions for $x^3 - 1 = 0$ in mod 7 and the coefficients on y are 1, 4, and 7 which we determined were the solutions for $x^3 - 1 = 0$ in mod 9.

9. The prime factorization of 63 is $63 = 3^2 \cdot 7$. Since 7 and 9 are relatively prime, we know that any number that is a solution to a given equation in both mod 7 and mod 9 must be a solution in mod 63. 7 and 9 are small enough numbers that we

can simply check each possible value by hand to determine solutions in mods 7 and 9. Then we can apply the method from the boxed problem of this problem set to determine which values are solutions in both mod 7 and mod 9 and thus mod 63.

10. The number of solutions to a given equation in mod n seems to be multiplicative. For an equation in mod 63, we can find the number of solutions in mod 7 and the number of solutions in mod 9, then multiply these values together.

11. We first note that $105 = 3 \cdot 5 \cdot 7$. We begin by solving the equation in each of these mods first.

    - In mod 3, the equation becomes $x^2 + x = 0$ in mod 3. In this case, the solutions are $x = 0$ and $x = 2$.
    - In mod 5, the equation becomes $x^2 + x = 1$ in mod 5. In this case, the only solution is $x = 2$.
    - In mod 7, the equation remains $x^2 + x = 6$. In this case, the solutions are $x = 2$ and $x = 4$.

    Now we will determine the solutions in mod 15. We know that any solution has to be 2 in mod 5, so our only possible solutions are 2, 7, and 12. Of these, 2 is 2 in mod 3 and 12 is 0 in mod 3 (0 and 2 being our solutions in mod 3), so 2 and 12 are our solutions in mod 15.

    Now that we have our solutions in mod 15 and mod 7, we will apply the method of the boxed problem to find our solutions in mod 105. We will **bold** solutions in mod 15 and *italicize* solutions in mod 7. The solutions in mod 105 are those numbers that are both ***italicized and bold***.

0	1	2	3	4	5	6	7	8	9	10	11	12	13	14
15	16	**17**	*18*	19	20	21	22	23	24	25	26	**27**	28	29
30	31	**32**	33	34	35	36	*37*	38	*39*	40	41	**42**	43	*44*
45	*46*	**47**	48	49	50	*51*	52	*53*	54	55	56	**57**	*58*	59
60	61	**62**	63	64	*65*	66	*67*	68	69	70	71	**72**	73	74
75	76	**77**	78	*79*	80	*81*	82	83	84	85	*86*	**87**	*88*	89
90	91	**92**	93	94	*95*	96	97	98	99	*100*	101	***102***	103	104

Thus our solutions are 2, 32, 72, and 102.

12. First we notice that the prime factorization of 1155 is $1155 = 3 \cdot 5 \cdot 7 \cdot 11$. As we discussed in problem 10 of this Set, the number of solutions to an equation

in mod n is a multiplicative function (let's call the function f), so we will compute the values for each of the prime mods, then multiply the results.

- In mod 3, the solutions are $x = 1$ and $x = 2$.
- In mod 5, the solutions are $x = 1$ and $x = 4$.
- In mod 7, the solutions are $x = 1$ and $x = 6$.
- In mod 11, the solutions are $x = 1$ and $x = 10$.

We see there are 2 solutions for each of these. So

$$f(1155) = f(3) \cdot f(5) \cdot f(7) \cdot f(11) = 2^4 = 16.$$

13. The table below shows the values filled in. An extra row for a general prime power is also shown to demonstrate the pattern.

n	$\phi(n)$	$s(n)$
1	1	1
p	$p-1$	p
p^2	$p(p-1)$	p^2
p^3	$p^2(p-1)$	p^3
p^4	$p^3(p-1)$	p^4
p^k	$p^{k-1}(p-1)$	p^k

Problem Set 9

Opener

number mod 7	0	1	2	3	4	5	6	7	8	9
6	20	41	62	13	34	55	6	27	48	69
5	40	61	12	33	54	5	26	47	68	19
4	60	11	32	53	4	25	46	67	18	39
3	10	31	52	3	24	45	66	17	38	59
2	30	51	2	23	44	65	16	37	58	9
1	50	1	22	43	64	15	36	57	8	29
0	0	21	42	63	14	35	56	7	28	49

number mod 10

Along a given diagonal (from lower left to upper right), the numbers in the cell increase by exactly one for each subsequent cell. This makes sense, since if a number x is a mod 7 and b mod 10, then $x+1$ must be $a+1$ mod 7 and $b+1$ mod 10.

1. **a.** 7 is prime and a small enough number that we can simply plug in every possible value of x to solve. The solutions are $x = 2$ and $x = 6$ in mod 7.

    b. The solutions are $x = 2, 4, 7, 9$. These can be found directly, or by breaking up mod 10 into mod 2 and mod 5.

    c. We know that if a value is equal mod 7 to either 2 or 6 and that value is also equal mod 10 to 2, 4, 7, or 9, that value must be a solution to $x^2 - x - 2 = 0$ in mod 70 since we know $x^2 - x - 2$ is a multiple of both 7 and 10, which are relatively prime numbers. We can use the table to find every possible combination of our solutions from mods 7 and 10. This gives us the solutions $x = 2, 9, 27, 34, 37, 44, 62, 69$.

2. Here's what happens when you try to make a similar chart for 6 and 10:

5				11		23		5		17		29
4	10			22			4		16		28	
3			21		3		15		27			9
2	20			2		14		26		8		
1			1		13		25		7			19
0	0			12		24		6		18		
	0	1	2	3	4	5	6	7	8	9		

Notice that the next space we would put 30 in is already occupied by 0, so we can't fit all 60 numbers in. In particular, since $\gcd(6, 10) = 2$, we can never get to half of the spaces on the board.

3. **a.** This is the diameter of the circle, or $\frac{1}{4}$ as we determined in Problem Set 5 problem 10.

    b. Again, this is the diameter of the circle, or $\frac{1}{9}$ as determined in Problem Set 5 problem 11.

    c. The total length of the path is the sum of the diameters of all the circles. The diameter of the nth circle is $\frac{1}{n^2}$, so the total length of the path is this infinite sum:

$$\sum_{n=1}^{\infty} \frac{1}{n^2}$$

We don't know yet what this sum evaluates to, or if it even has a sum at all.

4. The shortest distance between two points is a straight line. Timon walks the shortest possible distance from point A to B, from B to C, and from C to D, so any curved path must be longer.

5.   **a.** The factors of 10 are 1,2,5,10 so

$$b(10) = 1 + \frac{1}{4} + \frac{1}{25} + \frac{1}{100}.$$

   b. The factors of 6 are 1,2,3,6 so

$$b(6) = 1 + \frac{1}{4} + \frac{1}{9} + \frac{1}{36}.$$

   c. The factors of 24 are 1,2,3,4,6,8,12,24 so

$$b(24) = 1 + \frac{1}{4} + \frac{1}{9} + \frac{1}{16} + \frac{1}{36} + \frac{1}{64} + \frac{1}{144} + \frac{1}{576}.$$

   d. All of the numbers 1 through 6 are factors of 60 so the first 6 terms of $b(60)$ are

$$b(60) = 1 + \frac{1}{4} + \frac{1}{9} + \frac{1}{16} + \frac{1}{25} + \frac{1}{36} + \cdots$$

   e. All of the numbers 1 through 10 are factors of 2520 so the first 10 terms of $b(2520)$ are

$$b(60) = 1 + \frac{1}{4} + \frac{1}{9} + \frac{1}{16} + \frac{1}{25} + \frac{1}{36} + \frac{1}{49} + \frac{1}{64} + \frac{1}{81} + \frac{1}{100} + \cdots$$

6.   **a.** We note that this means that any number that is a perfect square will have 2 solutions as in the sidenote (i.e. $f(9) = 2$ since $3^2 = 9$ and $(-3)^2 = 9$) with the exception of 0, which has only 1 solution (as $-0 = 0$). For any number that is not a perfect square, $f(n) = 0$.

n	0	1	2	3	4	5	6	7	8	9	10	11	12
$f(n)$	1	2	0	0	2	0	0	0	0	2	0	0	0

n	13	14	15	16	17	18	19	20	21	22	23	24	25
$f(n)$	0	0	0	2	0	0	0	0	0	0	0	0	2

   b. No, f is not multiplicative. In order for f to be multiplicative, $f(1)$ must be either 1 or 0. Since $f(1) = 2$, f cannot be multiplicative.

c. We created the "dice polynomial" by making the coefficient on x^n the number of different ways to roll n. Here, we will make the coefficient on x^n the number of different ways to write n as a perfect square, that is $f(n)$. This gives us the polynomial

$$1 + 2x + 2x^4 + 2x^9 + 2x^{16} + 2x^{25} + \cdots$$

7. a. We square our polynomial to yield

$$1 + 4x + 4x^2 + 4x^4 + 8x^5 + 4x^8 + 4x^9 + 8x^{10} + 8x^{13}$$
$$+ 4x^{16} + 8x^{17} + 4x^{18} + 8x^{20} + 12x^{25} + \cdots$$

Taking the coefficients to fill in our table, we have

n	0	1	2	3	4	5	6	7	8	9	10	11	12
$f_2(n)$	1	4	4	0	4	8	0	0	4	4	8	0	0

n	13	14	15	16	17	18	19	20	21	22	23	24	25
$f_2(n)$	8	0	0	4	8	4	0	8	0	0	0	0	12

b. No, f_2 is not multiplicative. In order for f_2 to be multiplicative, $f_2(1)$ must be either 1 or 0. Since $f_2(1) = 4$, f_2 cannot be multiplicative.

8. a. There are, as the problem statement implies, 4 ways to write 2 as the sum of two squares. They are

$$1^2 + 1^2 \qquad 1^2 + (-1)^2 \qquad (-1)^2 + 1^2 \qquad (-1)^2 + (-1)^2$$

b. There is no way to write 7 as the sum of two squares. $1^2 + 2^2 = 5$ which is too small, but $2^2 + 2^2 = 8$, $0^2 + 3^2 = 9$, and $1^2 + 3^2 = 10$ are both too big.

c. There are 4 ways to write 9 as the sum of two squares:

$$3^2 + 0^2 \qquad 0^2 + (-3)^2 \qquad (-3)^2 + 0^2 \qquad 0^2 + 3^2$$

d. There are 8 ways to write 13 as the sum of two squares:

$$2^2 + 3^2 \qquad 2^2 + (-3)^2 \qquad (-2)^2 + 3^2 \qquad (-2)^2 + (-3)^2$$
$$3^2 + 2^2 \qquad 3^2 + (-2)^2 \qquad (-3)^2 + 2^2 \qquad (-3)^2 + (-2)^2$$

e. There are 12 ways to write 25 as the sum of two squares:

$$4^2 + 3^2 \qquad 4^2 + (-3)^2 \qquad (-4)^2 + 3^2 \qquad (-4)^2 + (-3)^2$$
$$3^2 + 4^2 \qquad 3^2 + (-4)^2 \qquad (-3)^2 + 4^2 \qquad (-3)^2 + (-4)^2$$
$$5^2 + 0^2 \qquad 0^2 + (-5)^2 \qquad (-5)^2 + 0^2 \qquad 0^2 + 5^2$$

These values match up with the corresponding values of $f_2(n)$! Interesting...

Neat Stuff

9. **a.** Consulting our table, we find that $a = 21$.

   b. Again referencing the table, we determine $b = 50$.

   c. We can compute

   $$4a + 6b = 84 + 300 = 384 = 34 \bmod 70.$$

   Looking at our table, we find that 34 is exactly the number that is 4 in mod 10 and 6 in mod 7!

   d. We again compute

   $$7a + 2b = 147 + 100 = 247 = 37 \bmod 70.$$

   Looking at our table, we find that 37 is exactly the number that is 7 in mod 10 and 2 in mod 7, which agrees with the pattern from part c.

10. (a) This part is one we've done before in previous circle problems. We get from the formula that $2(17 + c^2) = (5 + c)^2$, which simplifies to $c^2 - 10c + 9 = 0$. This has roots $c = 1, 9$. The larger root corresponds to the circle we're looking for, so the diameter is $\frac{1}{9}$.

    (b) Plugging in $a = 4, b = 9$, we get $2(97 + c^2) = (13 + c)^2$, which simplifies to $c^2 - 26c + 25 = 0$. This has roots $c = 1, 25$. As usual the larger root corresponds to the circle we're looking for, so the diameter is $\frac{1}{25}$.

    (c) Plugging in $a = 9, b = 25$, we get $2(706 + c^2) = (34 + c)^2$, which simplifies to $c^2 - 68c + 256 = 0$. This has roots $c = 4, 64$, so the diameter is $\frac{1}{64}$.

    (d) Plugging in $a = 25, b = 64$, we get $2(4721 + c^2) = (89 + c)^2$, which simplifies to $c^2 - 178c + 1521 = 0$. This has roots $c = 9, 169$, so the diameter is $\frac{1}{169}$.

    (e) The roots we are getting are the squares of successive Fibonacci numbers. One can verify that this pattern will always hold by showing the identity

    $$2(F_{n-1}^4 + F_n^4 + F_{n+1}^4) = (F_{n-1}^2 + F_n^2 + F_{n+1}^2)^2.$$

    where F_i is the ith Fibonacci number. In fact, a slightly stronger statement is true and can be proved straightforwardly by expanding and matching terms.

$$2(a^4 + b^4 + (a+b)^4) = (a^2 + b^2 + (a+b)^2)^2.$$

11. The table below shows the values filled in. An extra row for a general prime power is also shown to demonstrate the pattern.

n	$c(n)$	$a(n)$	$d(n)$
1	1	1	1
p	$1 - \frac{1}{p}$	$1 + \frac{1}{p}$	$1 - \frac{1}{p^2}$
p^2	$1 - \frac{1}{p}$	$1 + \frac{1}{p} + \frac{1}{p^2}$	$1 - \frac{1}{p^3}$
p^3	$1 - \frac{1}{p}$	$1 + \frac{1}{p} + \frac{1}{p^2} + \frac{1}{p^3}$	$1 - \frac{1}{p^4}$
p^k	$1 - \frac{1}{p}$	$\sum_{i=0}^{k} \frac{1}{p^i}$	$1 - \frac{1}{p^{k+1}}$

12. The key observation to make is that the $d(n)$ function from the previous problem is always less than one, as can be shown using the table we found. Furthermore, we have already shown in past problems that $a(n)$ can assume arbitrarily high values. So suppose we have a positive real $k > 0$. Take an n such that $a(n) > \frac{1}{k}$, which exists since $a(n)$ is unbounded. Then $a(n)c(n) = d(n) < 1$, so $c(n) < \frac{1}{a(n)} < k$, as desired.

13. We begin by finding the prime factorization $3289 = 11 \cdot 13 \cdot 23$. Now we will find the solutions to $x^2 = 3$ in mods 11, 13, and 23. Since these numbers aren't too terribly large, we can do this by testing each possible value of x.

   - In mod 11, $x = 5$ and $x = 6$ are solutions to $x^2 = 3$.
   - In mod 13, $x = 4$ and $x = 9$ are solutions to $x^2 = 3$.
   - In mod 23, $x = 7$ and $x = 16$ are solutions to $x^2 = 3$.

At this point, we have a couple different options. We could build two tables as in the boxed problem from this problem set (the first containing, for example, mod 11 and mod 13 and the second containing mod 23 and mod $11 \cdot 13$). This is a valid method for solving the problem, but filling in 3289 cells is tedious and takes a long time. Also, if we were to have a problem with even larger numbers this method would quickly become infeasible.

Instead, we'll make use of the method seen in Problem Set 8 problem 8 and this Set's problem

9. We will find the number a in mod 3289 that is 1 in mod 11 and 0 in mods 13 and 23; the number b in mod 3289 that is 1 in mod 13 and 0 in mods 11 and 23; and the number c in mod 3289 that is 1 in mod 23 and 0 in mods 11 and 13. This will take a bit of computational work.

Let's start by finding a. If a number is 0 in mod 13 and 0 in mod 23, it must also be 0 mod 299 since 13 and 23 are relatively prime. The reasoning behind this is the same as the logic from problem 1b of this Set. Now we want to find a multiple of 299 that is 1 mod 11. Since we are only really interested in the remainder when divided by 11, we note that

$$299 = 11 \cdot 27 + 2$$

which tells us 299 is 2 in mod 11. This implies that 299k is 2k in mod 11 for any integer k. Since $2 \cdot 6 = 12$ and 12 is 1 in mod 11, this means $6 \cdot 299 = 1794$ is a in mod 3289.

We now find b and c in a similar manner. If a number is 0 in mod 11 and 0 in mod 23, it must also be 0 mod 253 since 11 and 23 are relatively prime. Now we want to find a multiple of 253 that is 1 mod 13. Since we are only really interested in the remainder when divided by 13, we note that

$$253 = 13 \cdot 19 + 6$$

which tells us 253 is 6 in mod 13. This implies that 253k is 6k in mod 13 for any integer k. Since $6 \cdot 1 = 66$ and $66 = 5 * 13 + 1$ is 1 in mod 11, this means $11 \cdot 253 = 2783$ is b in mod 3289.

Finally we determine c. If a number is 0 in mod 11 and 0 in mod 13, it must also be 0 mod 143 since 11 and 13 are relatively prime. Now we want to find a multiple of 143 that is 1 mod 23. Since we are only really interested in the remainder when divided by 23, we note that

$$143 = 23 \cdot 6 + 5$$

which tells us 143 is 5 in mod 13. This implies that 143k is 5k in mod 23 for any integer k. Since $5 \cdot 14 = 70$ and $80 = 3 * 23 + 1$ is 1 in mod 11, this means $14 \cdot 143 = 2002$ is c in mod 3289.

Now that we have $a, b,$ and c, if we wish to find a number mod 3289 that is ℓ in mod 11, m in mod 13, and n in mod 23, we can take

$$x = \ell a + mb + nc.$$

This makes sense since ℓa will be ℓ mod 11, but 0 mod 13 and 0 mod 23. Similar logic holds for mb and nc. We want to determine all x such that ℓ is a solution to $x^2 = 3$ in mod 11, m is a solution to $x^2 = 3$ in mod 13, and n is a solution to $x^2 = 3$ in mod 23. Considering all possible combinations, we have

$$
\begin{array}{cccc}
5a + 4b + 7c & 5a + 4b + 16c & 5a + 9b + 7c & 5a + 9b + 16c \\
6a + 4b + 7c & 6a + 4b + 16c & 6a + 9b + 7c & 6a + 9b + 16c
\end{array}
$$

which when we substitute in gives us

$$
\begin{array}{cccc}
1226 & 2799 & 1985 & 269 \\
3020 & 1304 & 490 & 2063
\end{array}
$$

as our solutions.

Problem Set 10

Opener

a. The factors of 4 are 1, 2, and 4. Thus,

$$b(4) = 1 + \frac{1}{4} + \frac{1}{16}.$$

b. From Problem Set 9 problem 3, we recall that the length of the path through the nth circle is $\frac{1}{n^2}$, which is also the diameter of the nth circle. This means $b(4)$ counts the part of the path that passes through the 1st, 2nd, and 4th circles, but none of the other circles. Thus $b(4)$ is less than the total length of the dotted path.

c. The factors of 6 are 1, 2, 3, and 6. Thus,

$$b(6) = 1 + \frac{1}{4} + \frac{1}{9} + \frac{1}{36}.$$

d. By similar logic to part 2, we realize that $b(6)$ counts the part of the path passing through the 1st, 2nd, 3rd, and 6th circles but none of the rest. Thus, $b(6)$ must also be less than the total length of the dotted path.

e. The factors of 12 are 1, 2, 3, 4, 6, and 12, so

$$b(12) = 1 + \frac{1}{4} + \frac{1}{9} + \frac{1}{16} + \frac{1}{36} + \frac{1}{144}.$$

This too is less than the total length of the dotted path; here we are only counting the segments through the 1st, 2nd, 3rd, 4th, 6th, and 12th circles.

f. By the same logic as in the previous parts, both $b(60)$ and $b(2520)$ are less than the total length of the path.

g. In Problem Set 9 problem 3c, we determined the length of the dotted path to be

$$\sum_{n=1}^{\infty} \frac{1}{n^2}$$

h. No matter what number you pick for n, $b(n)$ will be only part of the dotted path. The right side is the entire length of the dotted path.

1. The dashed path is longer. Like Timon's walk from Set 9, the dotted path is a straight-line path from one center to the next, while the dashed path is not.

2. The first section of the dashed path is the radius of the largest circle, which has length $\frac{1}{2}$. The remainder of the dashed path consists of vertical and horizontal segments between the point $(1, 1/2)$ and $(0,0)$. We know that the total distance travelled vertically (which is the same as the length of all the vertical segments) is $\frac{1}{2}$ and the total distance travelled horizontally is 1 (which is the same as the length of all the horizontal segments). Thus, the total length of the dashed path is

$$\frac{1}{2} + \frac{1}{2} + 1 = 2.$$

3. We determined that the dotted path is shorter than the dashed path. In problem 2, we determined the length of the dashed path to be 2. Since this is finite, and the dotted path length is even smaller, the length of the dotted path must be finite. More specifically, it must be less than 2.

4. In the Opener of this Set, we showed that for any n, $b(n)$ is less than the length of the dotted path. Since we know the length of the dotted path is finite from problem 3 of this Set, this means all values of $b(n)$ must be smaller than this finite number. Thus, there is a maximum possible value for $b(n)$, and it must be less than 2.

5. a. The numbers 1 to 9 that are relatively prime to 9 are 1, 2, 4, 5, 7, and 8. These are the numbers that contribute to $\phi(9)$.
   b. The "coordinates" of the products contributing to $P(9)$ are $(1,1), (2,5), (4,7), (5,2), (7,4)$, and $(8,8)$. Thus the rows and columns are 1, 2, 4, 5, 7, and 8, which are exactly the same numbers we found in part a.
   c. The numbers 1 to 10 that are relatively prime to 10 are $1, 3, 7,$ and 9. These are the numbers that contribute to $\phi(10)$.
   d. The rows and columns in which the products contributing to $P(10)$ occur are $1, 3, 7,$ and 9, matching the numbers we found in part c.

6. Although you can proceed as in Set 9, you can also shortcut the process by using the picture of the mod 10 multiplication table. The numbers we seek are multiples of 3, 7, and 9, but are also equal to 1 mod 10. Looking in the mod 10 multiplication

table at row 3, row 7, and row 9, you can find the numbers immediately.

a. $21 = 3 \cdot 7$

b. $21 = 7 \cdot 3$

c. $81 = 9 \cdot 9$

7. a. We examine each of these in turn. For each n we count the numbers 1 to n that are relatively prime to n. These are the numbers making up $\phi(n)$.

- $n = 1$: 1
- $n = 3$: 1, 2
- $n = 5$: 1, 2, 3, 4
- $n = 15$: 1, 2, 4, 7, 8, 11, 13, 14

b. We examine each of the sets in turn again.

- $n = 1$ ($\times \frac{15}{1} = 15$): 15
- $n = 3$ ($\times \frac{15}{3} = 5$): 5, 10
- $n = 5$ ($\times \frac{15}{5} = 3$): 3, 6, 9, 12
- $n = 15$ ($\times \frac{15}{15} = 1$): 1, 2, 4, 7, 8, 11, 13, 14

We notice that we end up with each of the numbers 1 to 15 exactly once.

c. We examine each of these in turn. For each n we count the numbers 1 to n that are relatively prime to n. These are the numbers making up $\phi(n)$.

- $n = 1$: 1
- $n = 2$: 1
- $n = 7$: 1, 2, 3, 4, 5, 6
- $n = 14$: 1, 3, 5, 9, 11, 13

Now multiply each by $\frac{14}{n}$.

- $n = 1$ ($\times \frac{14}{1} = 14$): 14
- $n = 2$ ($\times \frac{14}{2} = 7$): 7
- $n = 7$ ($\times \frac{14}{7} = 2$): 2, 4, 6, 8, 10, 12
- $n = 14$ ($\times \frac{14}{14} = 1$): 1, 3, 5, 9, 11, 13

Again, we notice that we end up with each of the numbers 1 to $n = 14$ exactly once.

d. Answers will vary, but should still result in seeing each number from 1 to n exactly once.

Neat Stuff

8. Circles of any diameter of the form $\frac{1}{n^2}$ for n a positive integer can be found. There will be $\phi(n)$ copies of circles with diameter $\frac{1}{n^2}$ constructed for $n > 1$. One way to think about this is to note that there will be a circle whose x-coordinate is any rational fraction $\frac{a}{n}$ between 0 and 1. The size of this circle is determined by the denominator of the fraction, but only when the fraction is in lowest

terms. In order for $\frac{a}{n}$ to be in lowest terms, a must not share any common factors with n, and this is exactly what $\phi(n)$ counts.

9. The pattern involves the dimensions of the right triangles. The largest right triangle has vertices $(1, \frac{1}{2})$, $(\frac{1}{2}, \frac{1}{8})$, and $(1, \frac{1}{8})$. The lengths of the sides of this right triangle are $\frac{3}{8}, \frac{1}{2}, \frac{5}{8}$, so this triangle is the same shape as the 3-4-5 right triangle.

    The second right triangle has vertices $(\frac{1}{2}, \frac{1}{8})$, $(\frac{1}{3}, \frac{1}{18})$, and $(\frac{1}{2}, \frac{1}{18})$. The lengths of the sides of this triangle are $\frac{5}{72}, \frac{1}{6}, \frac{13}{72}$, so this triangle is the same shape as the 5-12-13 right triangle.

    This pattern continues forever and can be generalized from the coordinates $(\frac{1}{n}, \frac{1}{2n^2})$, $(\frac{1}{n+1}, \frac{1}{2(n+1)^2})$, and $(\frac{1}{n}, \frac{1}{2(n+1)^2})$ and the corresponding side lengths of the triangle.

10. The center of each circle the parabola passes through can be found to have coordinates $(\frac{1}{n}, \frac{1}{2n^2})$. Therefore the equation of the parabola is $y = \frac{x^2}{2}$.

11. The parabola is a curved path from $(0,0)$ to $(1, 1/2)$ through all the centers, so its total length is greater than the dotted path from $(0,0)$ to $(1,1/2)$, made up of the radius of the large circle, plus the diameter of all the smaller circles:

    $$\frac{1}{2} + \sum_{n=2}^{\infty} \frac{1}{n^2}.$$

    Using calculus, the length of the parabola can be found to be about $1.14779\ldots$. By adding $1/2$, this gives a better upper bound of 1.64779 on the infinite sum

    $$\sum_{n=1}^{\infty} \frac{1}{n^2}$$

12. All of the circles can be packed into a rectangle with vertices $(-\frac{1}{2}, 0)$, $(\frac{3}{2}, 0)$, $(\frac{3}{2}, 1)$, $(-\frac{1}{2}, 1)$, which has area 2. So the total area of all circles is less than 2.

13. Using methods similar to those from Set 8 problem 14, we can show the point of tangency is $x = \frac{a+c}{b+d}$.

Problem Set 11

Opener

n	1	2	3	4	5	6	7	8	9	10	11	12	13	14	15
$\mu(n)$	1	-1	-1	0	-1	1	-1	0	0	1	-1	0	-1	1	1
$z(n)$	1	0	0	0	0	0	0	0	0	0	0	0	0	0	0
$m(n)$	1	1	1	1	1	1	1	1	1	1	1	1	1	1	1
$\tau(n)$	1	2	2	3	2	4	2	4	3	4	2	6	2	4	4
$u(n)$	1	3	3	6	3	9	3	10	6	9	3	18	3	9	9

n	16	17	18	19	20	21	22	23	24	25	26	27	28	29	30
$\mu(n)$	0	-1	0	-1	0	1	1	-1	0	0	1	0	0	-1	-1
$z(n)$	0	0	0	0	0	0	0	0	0	0	0	0	0	0	0
$m(n)$	1	1	1	1	1	1	1	1	1	1	1	1	1	1	1
$\tau(n)$	5	2	6	2	6	4	4	2	8	3	4	4	6	2	8
$u(n)$	15	3	18	3	18	9	9	3	30	6	9	10	18	3	27

1. Answers will vary.

2. The first ten numerators are
$$\frac{1}{1^s}+\frac{2}{2^s}+\frac{2}{3^s}+\frac{3}{4^s}+\frac{2}{5^s}+\frac{4}{6^s}+\frac{2}{7^s}+\frac{4}{8^s}+\frac{3}{9^s}+\frac{4}{10^s}+\cdots,$$
Notice this matches the τ function computed in the boxed problem. There is a good reason for this: we can notice that when computing the fraction with denominator n^s, we will add one in the numerator for every pair of positive integers x, y such that $xy = n$. The number of these pairs is $\tau(n)$ since there are $\tau(n)$ choices for x and a unique way to choose y from there.

3.   a. We first note that 5 and 1 have no common factors greater than 1. Since we can write $5 = 1 \cdot 5$ and we know f is multiplicative, we have

$$f(5) = f(1 \cdot 5) = f(1)f(5)$$

as desired.

   b. If $f(5)$ is nonzero, since $f(5) = f(1)f(5)$ we can divide both sides by $f(5)$ to find $f(1) = 1$.

c. If $f(1) > 1$, multiplying both sides by $f(1)$ we find $f(1)f(1) > f(1)$. In order for f to be multiplicative, it must be the case that

$$f(1)f(1) = f(1 \cdot 1) = f(1).$$

Since $f(1)f(1)$ is strictly greater than $f(1)$, f cannot be multiplicative.

4. We can fill in the table using the handout by counting how many times a given number appears.

n	0	1	2	3	4	5	6	7	8	9	10	11	12
$s_2(n)$	1	4	4	0	4	8	0	0	4	4	8	0	0

n	13	14	15	16	17	18	19	20	21	22	23	24	25
$s_2(n)$	8	0	0	4	8	4	0	8	0	0	0	0	12

5. a. s_2 is not multiplicative, since $s_2(1) = 4$ when $s_2(1) = 1$ is required.
    b. Based on the values of s_2 we have seen so far, S_2 seems to be multiplicative.

6. Squaring the polynomial yields

$$1+4x+4x^2+4x^4+8x^5+4x^8+4x^9+8x^{10}+8x^{13}+4x^{16}+8x^{17}+4x^{18}+8x^{20}+12x^{25}+\cdots$$

The coefficient on x^n in this polynomial is the value of $s_2(n)$.

7. a. Because $s_4(1) = 8$, s_4 is not multiplicative.
    b. Following the example we saw in problem 5b of this Set, divide by an appropriate value to make $S_4(1) = 1$. Thus, define $S_4(n) = \frac{s_4(n)}{8}$. Since $S_4(1) = 1$, $S_4(n) = S_4(1)S_4(n)$ for any n value. Let's check a few other values

$$S_4(6) = 12 = 3 \cdot 4 = S_4(2)S_4(3)$$

so this holds. We can also check

$$S_4(20) = 18 = 3 \cdot 6 = S_4(4)S_4(5)$$

so again S_4 behaves as we would expect a multiplicative function to. In fact, for all values in our table, $S_4(n) = \frac{s_4(n)}{8}$ behaves as a multiplicative function.

8. To determine the point of intersection, we can set the two equations equal:

$$y = rx + 1 = x$$

which, when we solve for x, yields

$$x = \frac{1}{1-r}.$$

Thus our point of intersection is $\left(\frac{1}{1-r}, \frac{1}{1-r}\right)$.
Note that each of these coordinates could also be viewed as the sum of $1 + r + r^2 + r^3 + \cdots$ as shown in the diagrams. Thus we have in fact derived the formula for the sum of an infinite geometric series. That is,

$$\sum_{k=0}^{\infty} r^k = \frac{1}{1-r}.$$

Neat Stuff

9. An effective method for determining a multiplicative function's behavior is by observing how it acts on powers of primes. While we have not definitively proved μ is multiplicative, it appears to be so for all values in our table. We will proceed based on the assumption that μ is in fact multiplicative.

    We first note $\mu(1) = 1$. Next we note how $\mu(p)$ behaves for primes p. We see $\mu(p) = -1$. For any greater power of a prime, that is $\mu(p^k)$ for $k > 1$, $\mu(p^k) = 0$. Now applying our multiplicative assumption, we see that if a number n's prime factorization contains a prime raised to a power greater than 1, $\mu(n) = 0$ since $\mu(p^k) = 0$ for that prime and all primes share no factor greater than 1 so we have zero times something. Now if n's prime factorization contains only primes to the first power (we call such a number "square-free"), then if $n = p_1 \cdot p_2 \cdots p_m$ for some m, then

$$\mu(n) = \mu(p_1) \cdot \mu(p_2) \cdots \mu(p_m) = -1 \cdot -1 \cdots -1 = (-1)^m.$$

10. Start with problem 8's result that

$$1 + r + r^2 + \cdots = \frac{1}{1-r}$$

    The only variation is that the first term may be some number a instead of 1. Just multiply everything through by a:

$$a + ar + ar^2 + \cdots = \frac{a}{1-r}$$

    Note that depending on the value of r, the sum may not exist: for example, if $r = 1, 2$, or -1, the sum does not exist.

11. Any values you choose to plug in for x (with $x >$ 1) and r (with $r \neq 1$) will work to verify the given formulas.

12. The table below shows the values filled in. An extra row for a general prime power is also shown to demonstrate the pattern.

n	$\mu(n)$	$z(n)$	$m(n)$	$\tau(n)$	$u(n)$
1	1	1	1	1	1
p	-1	0	1	2	3
p^2	0	0	1	3	6
p^3	0	0	1	4	10
p^4	0	0	1	5	15
p^k	0	0	1	$k+1$	$\frac{(k+1)(k+2)}{2}$

13. The first ten numerators are

$$\frac{1}{1^s} + \frac{3}{2^s} + \frac{3}{3^s} + \frac{6}{4^s} + \frac{3}{5^s} + \frac{9}{6^s} + \frac{3}{7^s} + \frac{10}{8^s} + \frac{6}{9^s} + \frac{9}{10^s} + \cdots,$$

We notice these terms match $u(n)$. In general it can be shown that if we take the expression $\sum_{k=1}^{\infty} \frac{f(k)}{k^s}$ and multiply it by $\sum_{k=1}^{\infty} \frac{1}{k^s}$, we will get $\sum_{k=1}^{\infty} \frac{g(k)}{k^s}$, where g is the child of f. For this problem, if we take f to be the τ function (see problem 2 of this Set), then g is the u function as seen in the boxed problem.

14. The right hand side needs to always be equal to 1, so therefore it is

$$\frac{1}{1^s} + \frac{0}{2^s} + \frac{0}{3^s} + \frac{0}{4^s} + \frac{0}{5^s} + \cdots,$$

This matches $z(n)$. In light of the explanation for problem 13, think about multiplying both sides by $\sum_{k=1}^{\infty} \frac{1}{k^s}$, and remember $z(n)$'s child is $m(n) = 1$.

15. First, let's rewrite the right hand side of the equation in a form we're more used to:

$$1 = \frac{1}{1^s} + \frac{0}{2^s} + \frac{0}{3^s} + \frac{0}{4^s} + \frac{0}{5^s} + \cdots$$

The numerators of this series are the terms of the function we referred to as $z(n)$. The missing numerators make up the parent function of z, which we know by now is $\mu(n)$. Thus, we conclude that the missing numerators have the form $\mu(n)$ corresponding to the term with denominator n^s.

Problem Set 12

Opener

n	1	2	3	4	5	6	7	8	9	10	11	12
ego(n)	1	1	2	2	4	2	6	4	6	4	10	4
id(n)	1	2	3	4	5	6	7	8	9	10	11	12
σ(n)	1	3	4	7	6	12	8	15	13	18	12	28

1. The first 10 numerators of the given expansion are 1, 3, 4, 7, 6, 12, 8, 15, 13, 18. These coefficients are the outputs of the σ function. This multiplication process can be used to turn a parent function (as a string of coefficients) into a child.

2. **a.** We can get $\frac{1}{12}$ by taking from the first factor the term $\frac{1}{4}$, from the second factor the term $\frac{1}{3}$, and from every remaining factor the term 1. This gives us

$$\frac{1}{4} \cdot \frac{1}{3} \cdot 1 \cdot 1 \cdot 1 \cdots = \frac{1}{12}.$$

b. Yes, the product from part a is the only way to get $\frac{1}{12}$. This has to do with the idea that the prime factorization of a number is unique. The prime factorization of 12 is $2^2 \cdot 3$. The only way to get terms of the form $\frac{1}{2^s}$ for $s > 0$ is from the first factor of the product. Similarly, the only way to get terms of the form $\frac{1}{3^s}$ for $s > 0$ is from the second factor of the product. This idea extends for any prime; say p is the mth prime. Then the only factor from which we can pull terms of the form $\frac{1}{p^s}$ for $s > 0$ is the mth factor of the product.
In order to create $\frac{1}{12}$, we must have the prime factors found above, we must pull the powers of 2 from the first factor, the powers of 3 from the second factor, and so on. Thus, due to the nature of this product and the uniqueness of prime factorization, there is exactly one way to construct $\frac{1}{12}$.

c. By similar logic, we conclude that there is exactly one way to obtain $\frac{1}{45}$. We first consider the prime factorization $45 = 3^2 \cdot 5$. We then pull $\frac{1}{2^0} = 1$ from the first factor, $\frac{1}{3^2}$ from the second factor, $\frac{1}{5}$ from the third factor, and $\frac{1}{p^0} = 1$ from all remaining factors to obtain $\frac{1}{45}$. By the uniqueness of prime factorizations, this is the only way we can get a term of the form $\frac{1}{45}$.

d. As before, we conclude that there is exactly one way to obtain $\frac{1}{17}$. We know that 17 is itself a prime. We then pull $\frac{1}{17}$ from the appropriate factor of the product and $\frac{1}{p^0} = 1$ for all other factors. By the uniqueness of prime factorizations, this is the only way we can get a term of the form $\frac{1}{17}$.

e. For a general fraction of the form $\frac{1}{n}$, we begin by finding the prime factorization of n. We then pull terms of the form $\frac{1}{p^k}$ from each factor of the product, where p is the prime corresponding to the given factor and k is the power of p in the prime factorization of n (note that this power may be zero).

f. Every term of the form $\frac{1}{n}$ appears exactly once in the resulting sum for every integer $n \geqslant 1$. This gives us the infinite summation

$$1 + \frac{1}{2} + \frac{1}{3} + \frac{1}{4} + \frac{1}{5} + \cdots$$

This is the harmonic series, seen before in Set 3. The result of this summation is infinitely large. Therefore, this product is infinitely large as well.

3. (a) Notice that $144 = 2^4 3^2 = 16 \cdot 9$. Therefore, we can obtain it by multiplying $\frac{1}{16} \cdot \frac{1}{9} \cdot 1 \cdot 1 \cdots$.

(b) In the first factor, all the denominators are a power of 2^2. In the next factor, they are all powers of 3^2. This continues on with each prime being used once. By the fundamental theorem of arithmetic the only way to write 144 as a product of square prime powers if $16 \cdot 9$. Therefore, in order to get a factor of 16 in the denominator, we must take the $\frac{1}{16}$ from the factor with the powers of 2^2. Likewise, to get a factor of 9 we need $\frac{1}{9}$. Then the rest have to be 1. So this is the unique way to obtain 144.

(c) 45^2 also has a unique way of being written as a product of square prime powers by the fundamental theorem of arithmetic, so by the reasoning in (b) there is just one way: $1 \cdot \frac{1}{81} \cdot \frac{1}{25} \cdot 1 \cdots$.

(d) 17^2 also has just one way: select 1s from all factors except also pick $\frac{1}{17^2}$.

(e) 20 cannot be factored into a product of square prime powers since it itself is not a perfect square, so there are no ways to obtain it.

(f) Write out the prime factorization of n^2 and pick out each prime power of the factorization in a factor of B.

(g) From the previous parts it can be seen that

$$B = 1 + \frac{1}{2^2} + \frac{1}{3^2} + \frac{1}{4^2} + \frac{1}{5^2} + \cdots.$$

This sum is finite and is less than 2, and so is the infinite product.

4.

n	1	2	3	4	5	6	7	8	9	10	11	12	13	14	15
$R_2(n)$	1	0	-1	0	1	0	-1	0	1	0	-1	0	1	0	-1
$S_2(n)$	1	1	0	1	2	0	0	1	1	2	0	0	2	0	0

n	16	17	18	19	20	21	22	23	24	25	26	27	28	29	30
$R_2(n)$	0	1	0	-1	0	1	0	-1	0	1	0	-1	0	1	0
$S_2(n)$	1	2	1	0	2	0	0	0	0	3	2	0	0	2	0

5. a. We notice that in our table, R_2 seems to repeat the pattern $1, 0, -1, 0$ every four numbers. Writing this in terms of mods, we have the simple formula

$$R_2(n) = \begin{cases} 1 & \text{if } n \text{ is } 1 \bmod 4 \\ 0 & \text{if } n \text{ is even} \\ -1 & \text{if } n \text{ is } 3 \bmod 4 \end{cases}$$

b. Using the rule above, we can first simplify the expression by eliminating all terms $R_2(n)$ where n is even (since in this case, $R_2(n) = 0$). This gives us the simplified expression:

$$R_2(1) + R_2(5) + R_2(13) + R_2(65)$$

We notice that all of these numbers is 1 in mod 4, so each of these evaluates to 1. Thus, the overall value of the given expression is 4.

    c. Because we know that S_2 is the child of R_2, we can compute $S_2(130)$ by computing the sum of R_2 evaluated on each of 130's factors. But this is exactly what we calculated in part b. Thus, $S_2(130) = 4$.

6. We will deal with three different cases.

   First, we examine the case where $p = 2$, the only even prime. In this case $S_2(2) = R_2(1) + R_2(2) = 1$.

   Next, suppose p is 1 in mod 4. Since a prime's only factors are 1 and itself, and since we know $R_2(n) = 1$ when $n = 1$ in mod 4

   $$S_2(p) = R_2(1) + R_2(p) = 1 + 1 = 2.$$

   Finally, suppose p is 3 in mod 4. Since a prime's only factors are 1 and itself, and since we know $R_2(n) = -1$ when $n = 3$ in mod 4

   $$S_2(p) = R_2(1) + R_2(p) = 1 + (-1) = 0.$$

   Writing this more compactly, we have for a prime p:

   $$S_2(p) = \begin{cases} 1 & \text{if } p = 2 \\ 2 & \text{if } p \text{ is } 1 \bmod 4 \\ 0 & \text{if } p \text{ is } 3 \bmod 4 \end{cases}$$

7. We know S_2 is the child of R_2. Thus $S_2(n)$ is equal to the sum of R_2 evaluated on each of n's factors. We know any even factors of n contribute nothing to the value of $S_2(n)$. Every factor that is 1 in mod 4 contributes 1, while every factor that is 3 in mod 4 subtracts 1. Therefore

   $S_2(n) = $ (the # of 1 mod 4 factors of n)$-$(the # of 3 mod 4 factors of n)

8. (a) $f(1) = 1$ is required.
   (b) Since $\gcd(3,7) = 1$, we have $f(21) = f(3 \cdot 7) = f(3)f(7) = ab$.
   (c) The divisors of 3 are $1, 3$, so $g(3) = f(1) + f(3) = 1 + a$.
   (d) Likewise the divisors of 7 are $1, 7$, so $g(7) = f(1) + f(7) = 1 + b$.
   (e) The divisors of 21 are $1, 3, 7, 21$, so $g(21) = f(1) + f(3) + f(7) + f(21) = 1 + a + b + ab$.
   (f) Yes. $g(21) = 1 + a + b + ab = (1+a)(1+b) = g(3)g(7)$. The argument can be made to work with any pair of relatively prime numbers, although the computations are significantly simpler if we restrict ourselves to two prime numbers as we did here.

Neat Stuff

9. The table below shows the values filled in. An extra row for a general prime power is also shown to demonstrate the pattern.

n	$\sigma(n)$	$\mu(n)$	$\phi(n)$	$\tau(n)$
1	1	1	1	1
p	$p+1$	-1	$p-1$	2
p^2	$1+p+p^2$	0	$p(p-1)$	3
p^3	$1+p+p^2+p^3$	0	$p^2(p-1)$	4
p^4	$1+p+p^2+p^3+p^4$	0	$p^3(p-1)$	5
p^k	$\sum_{i=0}^{k} p^i$	0	$p^{k-1}(p-1)$	$k+1$

Note that the definition for $\mu(n)$ in the last row only applies for p^k when $k \geqslant 2$. The values for the σ column can also be written as $\frac{p^{k+1}-1}{p-1}$.

10. Notice that we could think of this problem in a different way. Essentially what we are asked is to find the number of ways we can write the number on the right hand side of the equation as the sum of two perfect squares. But this is exactly what is determined by the s_2 function which we have seen before. We can take advantage of our experience with $S_2(n) = s_2(n)/4$ and the fact that it seems to be multiplicative.

    a. We want to determine $s_2(25)$. We see from the table in problem 4 of this problem set that $S_2(25) = 3$. Thus, there are $3 \cdot 4 = 12$ lattice points on this circle.

    b. We want to compute $s_2(65)$. We first note that the prime factorization of 65 is $65 = 5 \cdot 13$. Then we see

    $$s_2(65) = 4{\cdot}S_2(65) = 4{\cdot}S_2(5){\cdot}S_2(13) = 4{\cdot}2{\cdot}2 = 16.$$

    From this we can conclude that there are 16 lattice points on the graph of the given circle.

    c. We want to compute $s_2(1105)$. We first note that the prime factorization of 1105 is $1105 = 5 \cdot 13 \cdot 17$. We can take advantage of our work in part b as 65 is relatively prime to 17.

    $$s_2(1105) = 4{\cdot}S_2(1105) = 4{\cdot}S_2(65){\cdot}S_2(17) = 4{\cdot}16{\cdot}2 = 32.$$

    From this we can conclude that there are 32 lattice points on the graph of the given circle.

11. The terms in the summation on the right hand side of the given equation are of the form $\frac{S_2(n)}{n^s}$

from problem 4 of this Set. We have seen several times throughout the Sets that multiplying a series with terms of the form $\frac{a(n)}{n^s}$ with the series $(\frac{1}{1^s} + \frac{1}{2^s} + \frac{1}{3^s} + \cdots)$ yields an infinite series with terms of the form $\frac{b(n)}{n^s}$ where b is the child function of a. Since we know from problem 4 that the parent function of S_2 is R_2, we conclude that the missing numerators have the form $R_2(n)$ corresponding to the term with denominator n^s.

12.   The numerators form the μ function.

13.   Please reference Problem Set 11 problem 7 for the solution to this problem.

14.   It appears from the table in problem 13 that $S_4(p) = p + 1$.

15.   There are several patterns that can be noticed here, but the most significant one is the following: replace the first 1 with a $\frac{0}{1}$, the second one with $\frac{1}{1}$, and the kth appearance of n for $n > 1$ with $\frac{a_k}{n}$, where a_k is the kth smallest positive integer relatively prime to n. So for instance, this would change step 4's row into

$$\frac{0}{1}, \frac{1}{4}, \frac{1}{3}, \frac{1}{2}, \frac{2}{3}, \frac{3}{4}, \frac{1}{1}.$$

It can be proven that the numbers obtained in this way will always be strictly increasing from left to right. Furthermore, they will contain every fraction that can be written as $\frac{p}{q}$ where q is a positive integer less than or equal to the step number and $p \leqslant q$ is a nonnegative integer.

This sequence is known as a *Farey sequence* and has a lot of interesting properties, including a fascinating geometric interpretation. As just one example of their properties, if $\frac{a}{b}, \frac{c}{d}$ are two adjacent terms of a Farey sequence, then $|ad - bc| = 1$. Many books and online sources contain information on this sequence, so the interested reader can do research of their own.

As the remark on the margin indicates, there is also a connection to the tangent circle problems. Indeed, arguing through them may be one of the easiest ways to prove the sequence derived in the first paragraph is strictly increasing, given what we know now. Notice that if we replace each x in the table with $\frac{1}{x^2}$, the row for step k will list the diameters of all the circles with diameter at least $\frac{1}{k^2}$ in left-to-right order. The sequence we derived in the first paragraph gives their point of tangency with the line.

Problem Set 13

Opener

We have previously expanded this polynomial in Problem Set 10 problem 15. We will reference values from the table we created in that problem.

a. $s_4(4) = 24$.

b. The sum of 4 ± 1s squared is 4. Because order matters, there are four positions; in each of these positions we have two choice: a positive or negative one. This gives us a total of $2^4 = 16$ sums composed of all ± 1s.

Also, $(\pm 2)^2 = 4$. We have two choices for sign (positive or negative) and four choices for the position of the ± 2 (all other values must be 0 or the sum will exceed 4). Thus there are $2 \cdot 4 = 8$ sums consisting of one ± 2 and three 0s.

This gives a total of $16 + 8 = 24$ ways of writing 4 as the sum of four squares, which agrees with the value of $s_4(4)$.

c. Since $s_4(1) = 8$, s_4 cannot be multiplicative. If f is multiplicative and nonzero, $f(1) = 1$ is required.

n	1	2	3	4	5	6	7	8	9	10	11	12	13	14	15
$R_4(n)$	1	2	3	0	5	6	7	0	9	10	11	0	13	14	15
$S_4(n)$	1	3	4	3	6	12	8	3	13	18	12	12	14	24	24

n	16	17	18	19	20	21	22	23	24	25	26	27	28	29	30
$R_4(n)$	0	17	18	19	0	21	22	23	0	25	26	27	0	29	30
$S_4(n)$	3	18	39	20	18	32	36	24	12	31	42	40	24	30	72

1. We begin calculating terms of the resulting infinite series to find a series

$$\frac{1}{1^s} + \frac{3}{2^s} + \frac{4}{3^s} + \frac{3}{4^s} + \frac{6}{5^s} + \frac{12}{6^s} + \cdots$$

The resulting infinite series has terms of the form $S_4(n)/n^s$. From the Opener, we know S_4 is the child of R_4, consistent with results from previous problems.

2. Based on what we have seen in previous problems, we expect that if we multiply an infinite series with terms of the form $a(n)/n^s$ for some function a by

$$\left(\frac{1}{1^s} + \frac{1}{2^s} + \frac{1}{3^s} + \frac{1}{4^s} + \cdots \right),$$

the result will be an infinite series with terms of the form $b(n)/n^s$ where b is the child of a. We will now prove this rigorously.

Consider the term after multiplying through by the given factor with denominator n^s. For every divisor d of n, there is a fraction of the form $a(d)/d^s$ in our expression which is multiplied by $1/(n/d)^s$ in the given factor to yield $a(d)/n^s$. Every divisor of n contributes to the numerator, so the resulting fraction is

$$\frac{\sum_{d|n} a(d)}{n^s}$$

that is, the sum of a applied to all divisors of n. But this is exactly the definition of how we determine the child function. So we see

$$\frac{\sum_{d|n} a(d)}{n^s} = \frac{b(n)}{n^s}$$

and thus, we see the resulting infinite series has numerators corresponding to the child function of the original expression's numerators.

3. The rule is that if n is divisible by the square of any prime, $\mu(n) = 0$. Otherwise, if n is the product of k distinct primes, then $\mu(n) = (-1)^k$.

Using this, we can find $\mu(120) = 0$ since 2^2 divides 120, $\mu(5005) = 1$ since $5005 = 5 \cdot 7 \cdot 11 \cdot 31$, and $\mu(30030) = 1$ since $30030 = 2 \cdot 3 \cdot 5 \cdot 7 \cdot 11 \cdot 13$.

4. The missing sequence must be the parent of the sequence $1, 0, 0, 0, \ldots$. As seen in Set 11, the parent of this function is $\mu(n)$, the Möbius function, so that function gives the sequence of missing numerators.

5. We compute the first six terms of the resulting series to be

$$\frac{1}{1^s} + \frac{2}{2^s} + \frac{3}{3^s} + \frac{0}{4^s} + \frac{5}{5^s} + \frac{6}{6^s} + \cdots$$

It would appear that while the numerators in the first expression correspond to S_4 from this Set's boxed problem, the resulting product has numerators corresponding to R_4, the parent of S_4. The last factor has numerators corresponding to μ, the Möbius function. It would appear that this factor acts as the opposite of

$$\left(\frac{1}{1^s} + \frac{1}{2^s} + \frac{1}{3^s} + \frac{1}{4^s} + \cdots \right)$$

which we examined in problem 3 of this Set, yielding the parent rather than the child function. Logically this makes sense: in problem 5, the series corresponding to the Möbius function multiplied by the series corresponding to m (the function that is always one), yields 1, implying these series are, in some sense "inverses".

6. This is correct. Every term on the left side can be found in exactly one way from the infinite product on the right.

7. a. Yes, there will be a $\frac{1}{15}$ term in the product. It will be created by selecting a 1 from the first factor, the $-\frac{1}{3}$ from the second factor, the $-\frac{1}{5}$ from the third factor, and the 1 term from all remaining factors. The sign will be positive, since the product of two negatives is a positive.
    b. There will not be a $\frac{1}{18}$ term in the product. This is because the prime factorization of 18 is $18 = 2 \cdot 3^2$. In our infinite product, we can only have one factor of $\frac{1}{3}$, not the two we would need to form $\frac{1}{18}$.
    c. Because 17 is prime, we can just select $-\frac{1}{17}$ from the appropriate factor and 1 from all the rest. Thus the sign on $\frac{1}{17}$ is negative.
    d. There will not be a $\frac{1}{20}$ term in the product. This is because the prime factorization of 20 is $20 = 2^2 \cdot 5$. In our infinite product, we can only have one factor of $\frac{1}{2}$, not the two we would need to form $\frac{1}{20}$.
    To form $\frac{1}{30}$, we pull $-\frac{1}{2}$, $-\frac{1}{3}$, and $-\frac{1}{5}$ from their respective factors (and 1 from all others). This yields a negative sign.
    To form $\frac{1}{5005}$, we pull $-\frac{1}{5}$, $-\frac{1}{7}$, $-\frac{1}{11}$, and $-\frac{1}{13}$ from their respective factors (and 1 from all others). This yields a positive sign.

e. We notice that the denominators that will appear are exactly those numbers that are square-free (that is, they have no repeated primes in their prime factorization). The sign on a fraction with denominator n (assuming denominator n appears) is negative if n has an odd number of (distinct) prime factors and positive if n has an even number of prime factors.

f. The description in part e sounds familiar to a particular function, μ. In fact, it turns out that the result of the expansion is simply

$$\sum_{n=1}^{\infty} \frac{\mu(n)}{n}.$$

Neat Stuff

8. **a.** Consider the geometric series given by $\frac{1}{1-\frac{1}{p}}$. We know that

$$\sum_{n=0}^{\infty} r^n = \frac{1}{1-r},$$

so this means this expands to the geometric series

$$1 + \frac{1}{p} + \frac{1}{p^2} + \frac{1}{p^3} + \cdots$$

Overall, this gives us an infinite product

$$\frac{1}{M} \left(1 + \frac{1}{2} + \frac{1}{4} + \frac{1}{8} + \cdots\right)$$
$$\cdot \left(1 + \frac{1}{3} + \frac{1}{9} + \frac{1}{27} + \cdots\right)$$
$$\cdot \left(1 + \frac{1}{5} + \frac{1}{25} + \frac{1}{5^3} + \cdots\right)$$
$$\cdot \left(1 + \frac{1}{7} + \frac{1}{49} + \frac{1}{7^3} + \cdots\right) \cdots$$
$$\cdot \left(1 + \frac{1}{p} + \frac{1}{p^2} + \frac{1}{p^3} + \cdots\right) \cdots$$

Looks familiar...

b. In Problem Set 12 problem 2, we found that this product results in the infinite sum

$$1 + \frac{1}{2} + \frac{1}{3} + \frac{1}{4} + \frac{1}{5} + \cdots$$

c. $\frac{1}{M}$ is infinite: it is the sum of the harmonic series. If $\frac{1}{M}$ is infinite, this means M, the reciprocal, must be 0.

9. We begin by checking the values from problem 8. We notice that there are no terms for any of the given fractions in the resulting product. However, for each term $\frac{1}{n}$ that did exist in M from problem 8, we now have a term $\frac{1}{n^2}$ with the same sign.

This implies the denominators that will appear are those that are exactly the square of a square-free number or to look at it another way, a number such that the power on every prime in its prime factorization is 2. Because the sign for the term with denominator n^2 in N is identical to the sign on the term with denominator n in M, we can conclude that the expansion of N is

$$\sum_{n=1}^{\infty} \frac{\mu(n)}{n^2}.$$

Now consider $\frac{1}{N}$:

$$\frac{1}{N} = \left(\frac{1}{1-\frac{1}{2^2}}\right)\left(\frac{1}{1-\frac{1}{3^2}}\right)\left(\frac{1}{1-\frac{1}{5^2}}\right)\left(\frac{1}{1-\frac{1}{7^2}}\right)\cdots$$

Each term $\frac{1}{1-\frac{1}{p^2}}$ expands to

$$1 + \frac{1}{p^2} + \frac{1}{p^4} + \frac{1}{p^6} + \cdots$$

Overall, this gives us the infinite product

$$\frac{1}{M} = \left(1 + \frac{1}{4} + \frac{1}{16} + \frac{1}{64} + \cdots\right)$$
$$\cdot \left(1 + \frac{1}{9} + \frac{1}{81} + \frac{1}{729} + \cdots\right)$$
$$\cdot \left(1 + \frac{1}{25} + \frac{1}{625} + \frac{1}{5^6} + \cdots\right)$$
$$\cdot \left(1 + \frac{1}{49} + \frac{1}{2401} + \frac{1}{7^6} + \cdots\right)\cdots$$
$$\cdot \left(1 + \frac{1}{p^2} + \frac{1}{p^4} + \frac{1}{p^6} + \cdots\right)\cdots$$

This is exactly the right side of the equation in problem 7. Therefore

$$\frac{1}{N} = 1 + \frac{1}{2^2} + \frac{1}{3^2} + \frac{1}{4^2} + \cdots$$

We can evaluate this using the aid of a calculator, computer, or website to find

$$\frac{1}{N} = \frac{\pi^2}{6}.$$

This tells us that while $M = 0$, $N = \frac{6}{\pi^2}$.

10. (a) Each one is a multiple of 2 with probability $\frac{1}{2}$. So the probability both of them are is $\frac{1}{2} \cdot \frac{1}{2} = \frac{1}{4}$.

   (b) This is the complement of the situation in (a), so the answer is $1 - \frac{1}{4} = \frac{3}{4}$.

   (c) By reasoning similar to (a), the probability both are a multiple of 3 is $\frac{1}{9}$. Then the probability one is not a multiple of 3 is $\frac{8}{9}$.

   (d) The probability two numbers don't have a common factor of n is the same as asking for the probability they are not both multiples of n. Here $n = 5$. By the work in the previous parts, the probability is $\frac{24}{25}$.

   (e) In general, the probability is $1 - \frac{1}{p^2}$ or $\frac{p^2-1}{p^2}$.

   (f) We can compute this by taking the product of the answers in (b), (c), (d) since these are independent events. Then we get $\frac{3}{4} \cdot \frac{8}{9} \cdot \frac{24}{25}$. Perhaps a more illuminating form is

   $$\left(1 - \frac{1}{2^2}\right)\left(1 - \frac{1}{3^2}\right)\left(1 - \frac{1}{5^2}\right).$$

   (g) Using the method of the previous problem, the result is the infinite product

   $$\left(1 - \frac{1}{2^2}\right)\left(1 - \frac{1}{3^2}\right)\left(1 - \frac{1}{5^2}\right) \cdots \left(1 - \frac{1}{p^2}\right) \cdots .$$

   Using the result of problem 10, we obtain that the probability is $\frac{6}{\pi^2}$, which is a rather remarkable result.

11. The series is found by the τ function, the number of divisors of each n.

   We know from problem 3 that multiplying by the series with numerators corresponding to $m(n)$ yields the child. That is,

   $$S \cdot \left(\frac{1}{1^s} + \frac{1}{2^s} + \frac{1}{3^s} + \frac{1}{4^s} + \cdots\right)$$

   is the child. Then to get the grandchild, we multiply the child again by the $m(n)$ series to yield

   $$S \cdot \left(\frac{1}{1^s} + \frac{1}{2^s} + \frac{1}{3^s} + \frac{1}{4^s} + \cdots\right)\left(\frac{1}{1^s} + \frac{1}{2^s} + \frac{1}{3^s} + \frac{1}{4^s} + \cdots\right).$$

Since multiplication is associative, we could multiply the latter two factors together first. This gives us the series corresponding to the child of m, that is τ. So to get the grandchild of our series S, we must multiply by

$$\frac{1}{1^s} + \frac{2}{2^s} + \frac{2}{3^s} + \frac{3}{4^s} + \frac{2}{5^s} + \cdots + \frac{\tau(n)}{n^s} + \cdots$$

12. Suppose we have some infinite series S and we want to find the grandchild of the corresponding function. We saw in problem 6 that multiplying by the series with numerators corresponding to $\mu(n)$ yields the parent. That is,

$$S \cdot \left(\frac{1}{1^s} + \frac{-1}{2^s} + \frac{-1}{3^s} + \frac{0}{4^s} + \cdots \right)$$

is the child. Then to get the grandchild, we multiply the child again by the $m(n)$ series to yield

$$S \cdot \left(\frac{1}{1^s} + \frac{-1}{2^s} + \frac{-1}{3^s} + \frac{0}{4^s} + \cdots \right) \cdot \left(\frac{1}{1^s} + \frac{-1}{2^s} + \frac{-1}{3^s} + \frac{0}{4^s} + \cdots \right).$$

Since multiplication is associative, we could multiply the latter two factors together first. This gives us the series corresponding to the parent of $\mu(n)$. So to get the grandparent of our series S, we must multiply by

$$\frac{1}{1^s} + \frac{-2}{2^s} + \frac{-2}{3^s} + \frac{1}{4^s} + \frac{-2}{5^s} + \frac{4}{6^s} \cdots$$

13.

n	ggp	gp	parent of m	$m(n) = 1$	child of m	gc	ggc
1	1	1	1	1	1	1	1
p	-2	-1	0	1	2	3	4
p^2	1	0	0	1	3	6	10
p^3	0	0	0	1	4	10	20
p^4	0	0	0	1	5	15	35

Problem Set 14

Opener

There are many ways to compute the appropriate values of $s_2(n)$. Here are the averages, rounded to four decimal places when needed.

1. as n goes from 1 to 25: 3.2

2. as n goes from 1 to 49: 3.0204

3. as n goes from 1 to 75: 3.2

4. as n goes from 1 to 108: 3.1481

The average as n goes from 1 to 1000 is 3.148. These averages are very close to π...

You can use the handout from Set 11 to shade all the elements of $s_2(n)$ for n from 1 to any value, and the set looks increasingly like a circle. For n, the radius of the circle is $\sqrt{n}$, and the area of the circle is πn. The elements don't precisely form a circle, so this is approximate, but it's a good explanation of why the average remains close to π.

1. This has to do with the existence and uniqueness of prime factorizations (for every positive integer but 1). Let's deal with the 1 first. By selecting the 1 from each factor on the right hand side of the equation, we get a product of 1. Because all numerators in the factors are 1, there will be no way to eliminate denominators in any other case to obtain an integer. So we have exactly 1 as an integer on the left hand side.

   Now, consider a number n. We know n has some unique prime factorization $p_1^{k_1} \cdot p_2^{k_2} \cdots p_m^{k_m}$. Thus we can construct it from the factors on the right hand side by selecting $\frac{1}{p_a^{k_a s}}$ from the appropriate factor. Because all primes are in seperate factors, the only way to obtain a given denominator n^s is by picking exactly those fractions with denominators corresponding to the prime factors and picking 1 from all remaining factors. Due to uniqueness, the numerator for any n^s must be exactly 1.

2. All the infinite sums have the form

$$1 + \frac{1}{p^s} + \frac{1}{p^{2s}} + \frac{1}{p^{3s}} + \frac{1}{p^{4s}} + \cdots$$

These are geometric series with ratio $\frac{1}{p^s}$. The sum is

$$S = \frac{1}{1 - \frac{1}{p^s}} = \frac{1}{\frac{p^s - 1}{p^s}} = \frac{p^s}{p^s - 1}.$$

Thus we can write

$$1 + \frac{1}{2^s} + \frac{1}{3^s} + \frac{1}{4^s} + \cdots = \left(\frac{2^s}{2^s - 1}\right)\left(\frac{3^s}{3^s - 1}\right)\left(\frac{5^s}{5^s - 1}\right)\cdots\left(\frac{p^s}{p^s - 1}\right)\cdots$$

3. Subbing in, we have

$$1 + \frac{1}{2} + \frac{1}{3} + \frac{1}{4} + \cdots = \left(\frac{2}{2 - 1}\right)\left(\frac{3}{3 - 1}\right)\left(\frac{5}{5 - 1}\right)\cdots\left(\frac{p}{p - 1}\right)\cdots$$

We know from previous discussions that the left hand side of the equation is the harmonic series, whose sum is infinite.

If there were finitely many primes, the right side of this equation would be a specific, finite number. This is a contradiction, so there must be infinitely many primes.

4. The first few terms of the expansion are

$$\frac{1}{1^s} + \frac{-1}{2^s} + \frac{-1}{3^s} + \frac{0}{4^s} + \frac{-1}{5^s} + \frac{1}{6^s} + \frac{-1}{7^s}\cdots$$

Note that only terms with no squares in their denominators will appear, and the coefficients of those that do will be 1 or -1 depending on the number of primes. This is exactly how the Möbius function μ is defined.

5. From Problem Set 13 problem 3, you know that multiplying a series through by

$$\left(\frac{1}{1^s} + \frac{1}{2^s} + \frac{1}{3^s} + \frac{1}{4^s} + \cdots\right)$$

yields a series corresponding to the child function of the original series. We know the child of $\mu(n)$, the function represented by the first series here, is $z(n)$, which is 1 from $n = 0$ and 0 for all other n values. Thus the right hand side of this equation is amazingly 1. This can be verified by direct multiplication.

6. Take the results of the last two problems, setting $s = 2$. From problem 4 we see that this product's terms will be in the form

$$\frac{\mu(n)}{n^2}$$

From problem 5, we see that this value, whatever it is, is the reciprocal of the sum

$$1 + \frac{1}{4} + \frac{1}{9} + \cdots + \frac{1}{n^2} + \cdots = \frac{\pi^2}{6}$$

Therefore, the product is $\frac{6}{\pi^2}$.

Neat Stuff

7. Notice that $\sum_{k=1}^{n} s_2(k)$ is equal to the number of pairs of integers (x, y) such that $x^2 + y^2 \leqslant n$. Also notice that $x^2 + y^2$ is the distance of the point (x, y) to the origin $(0, 0)$ in the Cartesian plane. Therefore, $\sum_{k=1}^{n} s_2(k)$ is equal to the number of points with integer coordinates, or lattice points, contained inside or on the circle of radius $\sqrt{n}$ that is centered at the origin. As n goes to infinity, the number of lattice points gets arbitrarily close to the area of the circle $n\pi$. Therefore, $\lim_{n \to \infty} \frac{\sum_{k=1}^{n} s_2(k)}{n} = \pi$.

8. (a) Answers will vary, but most of the pairs should turn out to be relatively prime. The next most likely outcome is 2.

   (b) For the GCD of two large numbers to be 2, each must be written in the form $2a$ and $2b$ such that a and b are relatively prime. This is $\frac{1}{4}$ as likely as picking numbers with GCD 1.

   (c) It's 9 times more likely.

   (d) It's 16 times more likely.

   (e) If the probability that the result is 1 is p, then

   $$p + \frac{p}{4} + \frac{p}{9} + \frac{p}{16} + \cdots + \frac{p}{n^2} + \cdots = 1$$

   The right side is 1 since there must be some GCD for any two numbers. Factoring out p shows that it must be equal to the same number found earlier, $\frac{6}{\pi^2}$.

9. In Problem Set 12, we computed a function R_2 which was equal to 1 on numbers 1 mod 4 and -1 on numbers 3 mod 4. R_2 was such that $S_2(n) = s_2(n)/4$ was the number of ways to write n as the sum of two squares divided by 4. Clearly since it counts something $S_2(n) \geqslant 0$. Suppose n had k_1 divisors that were 1 mod 4 and k_3 divisors that were 3 mod 4. Then for any n,

$$S_2(n) = \sum_{d|n} R_2(d) = k_1 \cdot 1 + k_3 \cdot (-1) \geqslant 0,$$

so therefore $k_1 \geqslant k_3$ for all n as desired.

10.   **a.** $A = \pi r^2$
      b. $V = \dfrac{4}{3}\pi r^3$
      c. $V = \dfrac{\pi^2}{2} r^4$

11.   Here are the averages:

      a. as n goes from 1 to 25: 124.8
      b. as n goes from 1 to 49: 241.4694
      c. as n goes from 1 to 75: 377.1733
      d. as n goes from 1 to 108: 537.5555

      The result from 1 to 10000 is 49349.064. The average of s_4 continues to grow and become unbounded.

      However, the ratio of the sum of s_4 compared to n^2 instead of n converges:

      $$\frac{\displaystyle\sum_{k=1}^{n} s_4(k)}{n^2} = \ldots$$

      a. When $n = 25$: 4.992
      b. When $n = 49$: 4.928
      c. When $n = 75$: 5.029
      d. When $n = 108$: 4.977
      e. When $n = 10000$: 4.9349

      These values converge...but to what? The key is in problem 10: the values converge to $\frac{\pi^2}{2}$. The reason the squaring of n is necessary is that the equation for the sum of squares, $a^2 + b^2 + c^2 + d^2 = n^2$, is four-dimensional in the variables a through d, but only two-dimensional in relation to n. This suggests s_4 should grow in proportion to n^2 and not n.